MW00616596

Sterling Script

A Local Author Collection
2021

Walper Publishing
Sterling Heights, Michigan

Editors
Tuesday Morning Writers
Rena Davis, Katy Hojnacki,
Terry Hojnacki, and Rebecca Eve Schweitzer

Editor-in-Chief
Terry Hojnacki

Cover Art & Design
Katy Hojnacki

All rights reserved.
Copyright 2021 Walper Publishing
Printed in the United States of America

ISBN: 978-1-949224-07-8
Volume Four of the Local Author Collection

No part of this collection may be reproduced, distributed, or transmitted in any form or by any means, without the prior written permission of the publisher, except in the case of brief quotations embodied in critical reviews and certain other noncommercial uses permitted by copyright law.

This book contains works of fiction, poetry, or nonfiction. The names, characters, places, and incidents in the fictional writings are imaginary and are not intended to reference specific places or people. Any resemblance to actual events, locations, or people, living or dead is entirely coincidental. The views expressed in the nonfiction works herein are solely those of the authors and do not represent the opinions or thoughts of the publisher or the editors.

The selections printed in this collection reflect the authors'
original work as submitted to the
Local Author Collection.

First Edition
1 2 3 4 5 6 7 8 9 10

Many thanks
to the authors and editors
in our vibrant writing community
for making this project possible—
again and again and again.

Happy Writing

Table of Contents

Dear Reader,

I am both proud and amazed as I hold this fourth edition of *Sterling Script: A Local Author Collection.* We're growing. Each year, we receive more submissions and more interest in our book. My team of editors, who volunteer their time and talent for this project through many challenging adventures, deserve my sincere thanks and gratitude. Together, we strive to encourage our local writers by publishing their short stories, poetry, creative non-fiction, and art.

The ongoing community support for this project continues to drive our mission. Quirky characters, emotional wonder, and unexpected endings are part of the creative contributions waiting for you in this collection.

As Nathaniel Hawthorne said, "Good reading is damn hard writing." Our authors have put in the hard work writing.

Happy Reading,
Terry

Teresa Moy

Teresa Moy is a technical writer, tai chi and qigong instructor, and lover of learning. She graduated from California State University, Sacramento, with a degree in English.

Her first published short stories appeared in *Sterling Script: A Local Author Collection* (2019 and 2020 editions). Currently, she's focused on writing her novella, *Chasm Awakening*.

Teresa is a member of the Sterling Heights Creative Writers Workshop. She enjoys sampling new cuisines, hiking Michigan's beautiful state parks, and dreaming about exotic lands far away.

Freeing Dragonflies

Teresa Moy

"Don't just stand there poking at each other! Help me bring in the groceries!" said Mom.

"Okay." Miles jabbed me one more time.

As I trailed my brother's footsteps toward the trunk of the car, a flash of bright blue alongside the garage caught my attention, and I stopped to investigate. Entangled in a network of silken fibers, a defeated dragonfly awaited his fate.

"Look what's stuck in a spider's web!" I squatted for a closer look. Our black-eyed Susans must have lured him from our backyard pond, and he collided with the sticky trap before he knew what happened.

Miles set down his grocery bag and dashed over.

The four-winged insect alternated between frantic wiggling and tired stillness. I imagined him cursing our neglect, since webs adorned several corners of our house exterior. When the spider returned to his fractal handiwork, he'd salivate over his colorful meal.

"Poor little guy." I rose and turned around to leave.

"Chloe, we should free him. Dragonflies hunt down and eat the mosquitoes in our yard. That's their job." My brother extracted the insect, careful to keep his delicate body intact, and set him on the pavement.

But the stringy tapestry had folded his tail-like abdomen in half. Instead of fleeing the scene, he slumped on the ground, fretting over his hapless predicament.

"Oh, no!"

"He'll be fine," I said. "I'm sure he can figure out how to untangle himself."

Mom came over and scrunched her nose at the tiny creature; she disliked all crawling, jumping, and flying pests. "Nature has probably given it special skills to help in these situations. Stop dawdling, Miles, and bring in the groceries." She shifted the bag on her hip and walked inside.

My brother, however, didn't give the insect as much credit as we did. I watched with awe and fascination as he crouched on the driveway and pulled the sticky strands off the dragonfly's abdomen until each segment straightened.

As we waited for him to take flight, he fell over on his side, twitching and squirming.

"What's the matter now? Why can't he fly?"

"Look," I said, pointing. "His legs and wings are also stuck together."

Of the two of us, my brother had the worse eyesight. He leaned closer to the distressed creature until his nose was a few inches away.

"He must have gotten wrapped in those strands when trying to escape. This will require more work—he's in a big silly-string mess."

"Really?" I whined. "I'm hungry. Let's go inside. Mom probably has the crackers out already."

"Do you think they bite?"

"What? I don't know."

He rummaged in the garage for a screwdriver and put on working gloves. He returned and knelt beside the dragonfly. "Okay, little guy, don't be scared."

"Miles! Groceries!" The elevated pitch in Mom's voice signaled that her patience was eroding.

He placed the insect in his gloved palm. With the screwdriver, he picked at the silky fibers to free his legs. In what I assumed was instinctive fright, the dragonfly flopped back and forth until he flung himself onto the ground. Miles

4

retrieved him and worked on his wings.

"How can you tell what you're doing?"

"I'm not sure, Chloe. The wings are so translucent, I'm having a hard time seeing them. I'm not sure I can separate them without tearing them apart."

"You're like a surgeon." I couldn't believe how much patience he had. No amount of foot tapping on my part expedited the process.

"Got it!" he said with a wide grin.

The insect darted away, using my brother's palm as a launching pad.

"You're welcome!"

"Nice job!" I patted him on the back. "I hope he's grateful and not just scared. You saved his life, and…oh, no!"

Mom came out to fetch more groceries, her stern eyes on my preoccupied brother, and our black and tan Shiba Inu bounded down the walkway. The insect skimmed near Luna's happy, gaping mouth and swooped through the open door.

"That was a close call! Do dragonflies typically fly near the ground or higher?"

"Again, I don't know."

"What the…?" said Mom as she re-entered the house. We heard banging and whacking in the living room, and her clomping footsteps announced how fast she was moving.

"No!" exclaimed Miles as we rushed through the door. "I just saved his life! You can't kill him!"

"Son, it's a bug, for crying out loud! If you'd just left it alone, it wouldn't be flying around in the house!"

Arms flailing, she climbed on the sofa, knocked over chairs, and ran into the coffee table. But the swift and agile dragonfly zoomed out of harm's way.

My brother grabbed his head in frustration. "Stop! Please, stop Mom!"

She didn't. "Dragonflies are a bad omen! Do you know what their nicknames are? The Devil's Needle! The Horse Stinger!"

"No, they're good luck! New insights, new beginnings? Prosperity and good health, and all that kind of stuff?"

Mom raced from the dining room to the upstairs bedroom. "Where are you, you little fiend? I'm going to get you!"

A hint of bright blue tore past us, and the insect hovered before our gold dragon painting which sat on the fireplace mantel.

"That's funny. Do you think he used to be a dragon?"

I giggled. "He's saying, 'Wow, I've sunk low on the food chain!'"

He glided along the mantel toward some black-eyed Susans in a glass vase. As he descended a leafy stem to investigate the water below the rim, my brother slid his hand over the vase, weaving his fingers between the protruding stems. The teeny creature flitted up and down, looking for an escape route. I hoped the insect wouldn't bite his hand.

We heard Mom thumping down the stairs.

"I have an idea!" I sprinted to the entryway.

As she reached the bottom stair, I opened the front door and slammed it shut. "There! He's gone!"

"Oh, whew! Thank you so much, Chloe!" With order restored, she returned to the kitchen to put away groceries.

Miles and I winked at each other. I reopened the door, and he removed his hand from the glass vase. The wee insect shot out, but like a boomerang, he whizzed back into the house.

"Are you kidding me?" I slapped my forehead.

The dragonfly sped around the living room, avoiding the kitchen where his potential killer was making a snack for us. We kept the door ajar and hoped he would understand the enormous hint. While he flew toward the entryway a few times, he refused to leave. Instead, some stray mosquitoes unwittingly invited themselves to the party.

"Kids, come and get your snack."

We left him to figure out his plan and went into the

kitchen to eat our crackers and cheese. Our eyes tracked the blue blur speeding past the arched doorway whenever Mom's back was turned.

As soon as she tended to some house chores, my brother grabbed his net and pursued the dragonfly, but to no avail. The insect could fly forward, backward, sideways, and upside down, and his abrupt change in direction left us stumbling over each other as we followed his erratic trail. He drifted in front of our noses, taunting us. The moment Miles lifted his net, the little thing zoomed away.

"What are we going do to?" he asked. "He's doomed if he stays in the house."

"But we can't make him leave."

"At least he's all set for dinner. I hope he finds those mosquitoes before they find my arm."

The rest of the evening, we spotted the insect darting around in our peripheral vision while steering clear of Mom and Luna. Maybe he weighed the dangers of the natural world against one human-sized female and an inquisitive, near-sighted dog and decided he could handle the latter pair.

After Mom went to bed, we tiptoed downstairs to the living room. The dragonfly streaked around the perimeter, stretching his four glorious wings. We assumed he was looking for dessert, since the mosquitoes had disappeared hours ago. With his bulbous, compound eyes, the small hunter spotted a few gnats congregating near some houseplants and inhaled them mid-flight. He settled once again by the dragon painting and crawled along the outline of his serpentine figure.

"I'm going to call him Indigo the Brave," Miles said.

The next day, we met after school so we could walk home together. I knew his creative writing class had selected editors for their writing categories and that both he and Leif, the most popular guy in the class, were running for fiction editor. Miles had thought Leif wanted the job to impress a girl in class; my brother wanted it to flex and hone his storytelling skills. I was eager to hear the voting results.

"Well?" I asked.

"Leif's the new fiction editor." He shuffled his feet against the sidewalk, his face framed with dejection.

"Oh, no! That's terrible."

"But...guess who he named co-editor?" My brother sang the words, beaming and fist-pumping the air.

I clapped my hands and skipped. "That's great! I'm so happy for you!"

"I asked Leif why he needed a co-editor. You know what he said? 'Because I know how much it means to you. You really love writing stories. I just want to cheer up my grandma, who's been sick.'"

"How thoughtful. It wasn't just about a girl after all."

"Yep. What a revelation. And now I'm fiction editor with the coolest kid in class."

When we arrived at our house, Mom was lying on the sofa, her arm draped over her face.

"What's wrong, Mom?" I asked.

"I argued with Taylor at work today, and we exchanged ugly, awful words. Then, after work, my car had a flat tire in the parking lot. I had to call someone to fix it so I could drag myself home!"

"Wow, what a rotten day!"

"It's all right, Chloe. I just need to rest, and then I'll get up and make you a snack."

"No, don't worry. I'll fix something."

Miles told Mom his good news while I went into the kitchen to look for munchies. I cut an apple and slathered peanut butter on the slices. Luna trotted in, her head raised with expectation, so I handed her one.

"Did your news cheer her up?" I asked as my brother joined me in the kitchen.

"No." He slouched into a chair, his eyes downcast.

"What? I thought for sure it would! What did she say?"

"She told me to help you with the snack." Miles shoved an

apple slice in his mouth, smearing peanut butter on his face. He dragged a napkin across his mouth and threw it on the table.

I extended a consoling hand, but he brushed off my sympathy like I was offering him a bowl of Brussels sprouts. I wished Mom wouldn't be so hard on him. "Did you see your friend?"

"Yup. He's hiding in the vase with the black-eyed Susans."

That night, I noticed my brother left his bedroom window wide open. His curtains billowed from the cool breeze, and chirping crickets echoed in the darkness. Indigo circled the room.

"Are you awake?" I whispered, stepping over the threshold.

"Of course."

"Are you giving Indigo a chance to leave on his own terms without being chased by a net?"

He sniffed and nodded. "If Mom finds him in the house tomorrow, she'll blame me and then squash him."

"She'll have to catch him first!"

Our winged guest hovered as if to say good-bye and skimmed toward the window. But he only devoured an errant mosquito before landing on the sill to survey his former territory.

In the morning, we were both elated and concerned to see our glittering friend racing around the room—another day we could enjoy his company, and another day that Mom or Luna could end his life.

I couldn't understand such loyalty from a tiny insect. Could he be that grateful?

Over the next couple days, Miles clocked his fastest time in track and earned a place on the state team. And although he typically suffered from insomnia, waking me up with his nocturnal hallway pacing, he was sleeping through the night. Meanwhile, Mom's clash with her co-worker escalated, and she caught a horrendous flu.

"Remember what you said about dragonflies? That they were good luck?" I asked.

Miles nodded, all smiles. "I'm having a fantastic week!"

"And remember what Mom said about them being bad omens?"

He nodded again, and then his eyes widened. "Oh, no! How could we both be right?"

"I don't know, but maybe…we have to free Indigo. For real this time."

"No! What about my editor job? The state track team? Sleeping through the night?"

"I know. Believe me, I'm getting more rest, too. But what about Mom getting a flat tire and her fight with Taylor? And now she's upstairs in bed with a high fever and chills."

He plopped on the sofa, a grimace distorting his face. "I know. You're right."

"Let's do it now, before you change your mind. We'll do it together."

We'd failed to catch him a few days ago, so we weren't optimistic about our current endeavor. His nimbleness and 360-degree field of vision afforded him an overwhelming advantage. As Indigo the Brave hung over a houseplant, Miles snuck behind him and swung his net. The dragonfly, however, saw it coming and bolted, circling the room and parking his body on the fireplace mantel under the dragon painting.

"I don't want to let him go," said my brother, admiring his pet's brilliant, splayed wings. He sighed and swung the net again.

"Do it like you really mean it, or else we'll be here all afternoon!"

For his part, Indigo treated this exercise as a game, swooping and flying at a dizzying speed. Guessing his capricious flight pattern was impossible. Our dog, though, raised the stakes by ambling in with a sizeable, bored yawn, and her squinty eyes locked onto the insect as he flitted over her head. Curly tail wagging with excitement, she chased after him. The dragonfly zipped upstairs, straight into Mom's bedroom.

"This is bad," said my brother as we ran after them.

We reached her room, leaning over and huffing. Luna, too short to leap onto the bed, scratched her front paws along the edge as she barked.

Mom pried one eye open. She had taken flu medication, so she needed a few seconds to focus on our faces. In a soft, slurred voice, she said, "What's going on, Miles? Can't you play downstairs?"

"It isn't my fault…"

Indigo hovered in front of her nose.

We cringed, expecting her insect aversion to jolt her from her haze. Her droopy eyes peered at him. I wasn't sure how much she could see, since she didn't have her glasses on.

"What in the world…?" Her jaw dropped, and she pressed her head against her pillow until it puffed around her ears. We waited for screaming and swatting to ensue, but she lied still with her hands resting heavily atop her floral comforter as if pinned to her bed. Why she wasn't flailing was a mystery to me. With deep, measured breaths, she stared at him until her face softened with wonder. "What a magnificent creature! And those mighty wings!"

I flicked a quick glance at my brother. The flu medication must have warped her insect sensitivity like fun house mirrors at a carnival.

"Yes, like fairy wings!" Miles suggested.

Our beloved pet alighted on the back of her hand.

"A good luck fairy to bring you good health and prosperity," I added.

Mom yawned. With her free hand, she picked up a cool, wet face towel on her nightstand and laid it across her sweaty forehead. "It certainly isn't a fairy. I could, however, use some good health and prosperity."

Indigo cocked his head as if he understood and rose above

her hand. Mom reached out to stroke his head, but either the dragonfly suspected she'd flatten him or his natural instincts kicked in, and he fled through the open window.

"Indigo!" Miles cried.

Although my brother had saved the dragonfly's life twice, the insect summoned his courage and returned to his native habitat. We scoured the yard and checked all the webs before clearing them with a broom. We hoped we hadn't replaced our good dragonfly karma with bad spider karma.

As I made scrambled eggs and toast the next morning, my mood sagged. I wondered if Indigo had embarked on a new adventure yet and if he missed us. The house lacked sparkle; even the black-eyed Susans drooped in their vase. I brought breakfast up to Mom, Luna scampering up the stairs behind me.

"How do you feel?"

"Much better!" She propped herself up to take the tray from me. "I think my fever's gone."

"That's wonderful!"

Mom ate her eggs while I poured orange juice in her glass. "Can you call Miles for me? I've been stressed at work and taken it out on him. I know becoming fiction editor meant a lot, and I just brushed it off."

"Of course!" I skipped toward the door.

"You know," she said, and I paused my messenger errand, "I had a weird dream yesterday afternoon. You, Miles, and Luna rushed into my room, and there was...a winged creature."

I smiled. "What kind of winged creature?"

"A blue dragon. He was so massive, he filled the room from floor to ceiling."

"What?" I gasped.

"When he flapped his wings, my hair blew back. At first I was afraid, but he wasn't a fire-breathing dragon. He had powerful, kind eyes that pulled the fever out of my body like a magnet."

12

My mouth flopped open.

"It was amazing. And then I realized it was my turn to pass on some good—to apologize to Miles and make amends with Taylor."

"Then…what happened?"

"Somehow, he squeezed his giant body through the open window and flew away."

I blinked several times, not believing my ears.

After I sent my brother to Mom's room, I walked to the backyard with some small, flat stones, intending to skim them across the pond. I strolled down the narrow path, threading my way between gnarly trees and overgrown branches and contemplating Mom's dream.

A faint, low rattle greeted my ears. Was it my imagination? When I reached the pond's edge, a swarm of dragonflies arose from the water—yellow, green, red, and brown ones beating their wings. They swirled in a tight mass, bobbing and twisting through the air like a flying serpent. A shimmering blue one lagged behind until the group enveloped him, and the insects vanished in the distance.

For Akoustic Chick: Soulful Rhythms

Teresa Moy

No apologies.
Piano, string bass, and drums,
The players cast their souls on an endless line.

Intricate and precise rhythms
Soar with beating wings,
Swirl like leaves in a benevolent whirlwind.

The shimmering notes cascade from the sky.
They dance and play, digress and reflect,
Ask curious questions and give sassy answers.

Each musician weaves his acoustic story,
Passes the torch to the next old friend.
Implicit trust launches a seamless transition.

How do I dissect their melodic language?
Understand the spell behind the magic?
Comparable to a misty fog, it flows by, cloaking its secrets.

Opening my heart, I surrender.
The layers of tones and silence
Wash over me like warm ocean waves.

The tide recedes, and I lasso the energy.
My pulse livens as I'm propelled from shore,
Triumphantly riding the crest when I return.

Tossed onto the beach, I'm dizzy with laughter.
Body still, heartbeat skipping, I lay on the sand,
Breathless.

Kathleen Belanger

Kathleen is an Oakland University graduate with a major in English. Her last position before retiring was with Master Card as a senior technical communicator. As a technical communicator, she has written and edited articles for newsletters, as well as technical manuals and business communications.

Kathleen enjoys creative writing and has participated in several critique groups throughout the years. Two of her short stories were runners up in annual short story contests sponsored by Oakland University for graduate students and alumni.

Kathleen currently participates in a critique group associated with the Sterling Heights Library.

Snow

Kathleen Belanger

He slipped away in the winter white
as the blizzard smothered the fields
outside the hospital window.

In the hollow of his eyes he watched
the man on the tractor
plowing out the parking lot.

He would do that
but the snow was running
through his veins now.

He covered up.

And the next day was cold.

Sonnet 180

Kathleen Belanger

At last we come to share the end of day,
Our passions cooled our love more temperate,
A wilting flower that blossomed once in May,
This tender bloom now begs an ending date.

But through our cloudy days the sun still shines
Though thoughts of future hopes and dreams
  have dimmed,
While strength and sight and hearing yet declines,
Green hedges turned to golden brown undimmed,

Old memories both good and bad now fade.
A passage long and days fulfilled have flown
To bring life's journey gently into shade.
And yet we look beyond what we have known.

For love lives on in places out of view
And in that place I'll come to beckon you.

A Crystal Dream

Kathleen Belanger

When all is dark on a winter night,
And moonbeams shed cold yellow light,
Snow fairies twirl white skirts around
And dance, dance dizzy to the ground.

They wave their silver icy wands
To frost the windows, trees, and ponds.
They toss their jewels upon the lawn
And play their silent games till dawn.

Then one by one they drift asleep
To make a carpet, thick and deep
That spreads across the countryside
And crests the hills like ocean tide.

The morning sun awakes to find
A world the fairies left behind,
A world of crystal fairy dreams
That sparkles white in sunlight beams.

John Stockdale

John writes fiction in various areas that interest him. He has written a memoir concerning his time at the Naval Academy and is currently working on historical fiction stories drawn from his family's history. Before his retirement as a CPA several years ago, he wrote numerous articles and a book in the field of business valuation.

John's hobbies are writing, sailing, hiking and fishing. He feels lucky to live in Southeast Michigan and lucky to live with his wife of fifty-two years.

Soul Secrets

John Stockdale

The decrepit Victorian made Richard Pincus shudder. An estate sale in a haunted house from a horror flick? But the blurb said they had a ton of old LPs, which drew him into one more creepy place, hunting for rare sixties soul music, an album so valuable it might change his life.

Creaky stairs led into the front parlor. The inside looked worse than the out, with a smell so acrid it warned away any person with common sense. He turned on his heel, but the stack of records stopped him cold. Today was his day for the find of a lifetime.

Maybe he'd find a pristine Arthur Conley, or a James Brown—with some luck, Wilson Pickett. After fifteen minutes he held an LP called *Soul Secrets* by Bruce True and His Soothsayers on the Deep-in-the-Soul label. Not a scratch on the disk and the cover immaculate. The artist never hit high on the charts, but he'd heard of Bruce, not this album though. Some collectors were after him, but Richard hadn't lucked into one before. His eyes glinted. This could be *it*, the one-of-a-kind worth thousands.

He had a motto—dicker down the dummies no matter what they asked. He'd offer the old crone running the sale a buck. She'd have no clue how valuable a platter like this might be. But when he looked at her wrinkled face, it seemed to change to the one he'd tried to forget. His body jerked. He dropped the five she wanted on the table and rushed out.

Just as he reached the door, her lips crunched up in a menacing smile and she hissed, "You'll find this one to be so much more than mere music."

His face blanched, and he wobbled out the door.

He skipped the other estate sales and drove straight home, his body shaking. The old witch might be right. This could be more than music. It could be rare gold that would change his life. He hurried in, sat down, and read the liner notes, written by Reverend Albert, pastor of The Greater Soul Purifying Temple. Yeah, right. Albert wasn't the Rev of any Temple. He was the record's producer playing on the word "soul." Still, the clever "Rev" had taken the ironic negative approach, "Brothers and sisters, do not listen unless you want to discover the true vibrations of the deep recesses of your soul."

Richard checked out the tracks. The first one—"Reach Into Your Soul," the second— "The Secrets of Your Soul," the artist's attempt to connect his soul music to the inner soul. If he'd carried it off, and with these liner notes, this sucker was worth a fortune.

Not that he believed a word of the inner soul religious claptrap. He smirked. If there was a soul, his needed to be purified all right. Dark secrets were hidden deep in those recesses.

His mid-sixties stereo had come from another estate sale last year. It needed a few minor repairs, like the frayed power cord, but it had a mellow sound you just didn't get from an MP3 player. Virgin vinyl like this deserved to be played on a classic system.

He eased the disk onto the turntable like it was about to break, then softly placed the needle. Fine old wax like this, you want to treat it like a baby. A bluesy beat pounded through the speakers, The Soothsayers thumping out a vibe that cut into his core.

This platter could be the most valuable he'd ever found.

How right that burned out old biddy had been. This might be more than he could imagine—the one to put him someplace different.

Her old face flashed in his mind, and again changed to the bitch whose image he'd buried way down deep.

That's when the lyrics slammed him.

> *Richard Pincus, time for you to reach into your soul*
> *Richard Pincus, clean up your sins before you grow old*
> *You been hidin' stuff way down low.*

He gasped at the sound of his name—and that weird lyric. The beat thumped on and Bruce True sang,

> *The things you done are evil*
> *and you got to fess up now.*

Richard grasped his chest, his legs shook, and he nearly fell to the floor. His hand quivering, he hit reject. Lifted the needle. And shut the system off.

But the beat throbbed on, and Bruce sang out strong,

> *It's time to clean up*
> *and clear out this muck you begun.*

He yanked the record off the turntable, broke it over his knee, then broke each half again. He picked up the pieces and the album cover, walked it to the trash outside, and headed back in, slamming the door behind him.

What the hell? The beat still shook the house and Bruce True wailed his lyric through the speakers,

> *Richard Pincus, stand up to the evil that you done.*

Richard screamed. What he "done" was best left buried. That bitch had had it coming. He grabbed the old stereo's electrical cord to yank it out of the wall. The frayed cord shocked his palm and he tried to loosen his grip, but his hand only tightened around it. He grabbed with his other hand to pull out the cord. The power surged up his arms and into his chest, then to his heart. His heartbeat ramped up, then pumped so fast his heart smoldered. Smoke poured out of his chest and his heart burst into blue flame.

The beat faded away and the last words Richard heard were,

> *Souls who won't repent their ways*
> *Owww!*
> *Will fry in an eternal blaze.*

Lucy Goosey

John Stockdale

Jimmy burst into the bathroom and shouted, "Grandma's mowing the front yard without any clothes on again!"

That shot any hope of getting to my client meeting on time this morning.

It had seemed like a no-brainer when I'd agreed Charlotte's mom could move in with us. Lucy had always been a sweet and proper lady, so I'd had no idea of just how wacky this was gonna get.

Damn, I hated this. I went out to the front yard and, sure enough, Lucy was pushing the mower, buck-naked, travel mug of bloody Mary in its holder on the mower handle. She was just turning the mower around giving me a full shot of her backside and then of full-frontal nudity.

Now, I suppose Lucy might look pretty good to a guy her age, eighty-five, but it wasn't my beverage of choice. You can be dead sure of that. Also I didn't need the police showing up to arrest her for indecent exposure again. We still had that court date coming up from last month's episode.

It's possible I could have put up with Lucy's shenanigans except for the bible-thumping religious fanatics across the street. They felt it was their solemn duty to call 9-1-1 for every little thing that happened. Take the time Lucy was having a party on the front porch with those drag queens she'd invited over. Where she met 'em I have no clue. What I did know was showing off their stripper acts was better done in the back yard. Still, the bible-thumpers might just have gotten a little carried away when they called the cops.

I hustled over and shut off the lawnmower. "Now, Lucy, we talked about this." I focused on her eyes in an attempt to avoid complete gross-out. "The neighbors across the street, some modicum of decency, the bad example for the kids."

Lucy eyed me like I was a little bit limited. "Look, *Dale*, it's already eighty-five out here with eighty percent humidity. It's all fine for you sitting in your fancy air conditioning, but us folk working outside have to adjust to current climactic conditions."

She did have a point, like she usually did. Which made me think she wasn't totally off her rocker. But I didn't get why it always ended up over the top. "Okay, at least put your swimming suit on."

"Hey, if it's good enough for those Russian miners I saw on TV to work in the nude. It's good enough for me. Besides, why should I be embarrassed about what God gave me."

#

The day of the court hearing arrived and I'd agreed to defend Lucy before old judge Smitherschutz. Lucy sashayed down the steps in an outfit showing a lot of leg and about as much cleavage as you could get away with and not show the whole upper structure.

"Now, Lucy," I said. "Do you think it's a good idea to wear that...revealing outfit? You're going before the judge for a preliminary hearing on a charge of indecent exposure. Perhaps a more appropriate choice of clothing is in order, particularly with a crotchety judge like this."

Lucy gave me that look again—only this time it was more like I was totally out of my mind. "My friend, Grada, told me about him. The only problem with my outfit is I might be covering too much up."

#

"Your honor," the prosecutor argued, "this woman was out in the front yard at 2396 Maple Lane completely unclothed at ten in the morning, deeply offending the neighbors and with an obvious intent to titillate."

Judge Smitherschutz eyed Lucy up and down. "Let me get this right, Mr. Prosecutor. You're telling me that this pleasant *eighty-five-year-old* lady intentionally exposed herself for the purpose of inflaming desire. Have I got that right? And some neighbor calls the police instead of her daughter or son-in-law." The judge winked at Lucy. "This court has better ways to spend its time than persecuting eighty-five-year-old grannies. This case is *dis—missed.*"

Lucy stood up and gave the judge a come-and-get-it smile and a little wave.

We walked out of the courtroom, Lucy doing the best wiggle-walk her eighty-five-year-old body could manage. I opened the courtroom door for Lucy and turned to look at the judge. His face was covered by a huge appreciative smile.

#

On the ride home, Lucy gave me a self-satisfied smirk and I had to admit I deserved it. "What is it you're always preaching about a great attorney?" she said.

"He knows the judge as well as the law," I muttered. "God knows you had a more effective presentation than what I was gonna argue. I'd heard rumors about Judge Smitherschutz's taste in women as he's nearing retirement, but my strait-laced self just couldn't accept it."

"We do need to talk about your strait-lacedness. Jump out of your box a smidge. Don't work so hard. Don't wait till you're north of seventy-five like I did."

"I take care of our Charlotte and the kids. We have our

fun. Nobody seems to complain."

"Maybe you oughta listen a little more closely to your kids. The fourteen-hour days just might not be working for them." She saw the time on the dash monitor. "Oh, gosh, it's almost noon."

"In a rush to get somewhere?"

"No worries, I still have time to change into my leather bustier. The motorcycle club is meeting at one. Harley's Elderly Angels are going to Hell—Michigan. Grada tells me she invited the honorable Judge Smitty along for a few brews at the Dam Site Inn."

Mark Morgan, Jr.

Mark Morgan, Jr. is a Detroit native, teacher, and poet. He enjoys meetings with the Poetry Workshop in Saint Clair Shores and the Creative Writers Workshop in Sterling Heights. His work is featured in the 2018, 2019, and 2020 editions of Sterling Script: A Local Author Collection, Angry Old Man Magazine, and The Rising Phoenix Review. Mark also won Landmark Books' Fourth Annual Haiku Contest in 2018. When not teaching or writing, Mark may be found reading, practicing martial arts, or listening to jazz.

Horror Show

Mark Morgan, Jr.

the future deals in moments burning like tiny meteors in our lungs and perhaps this is why i hold my breath as the curtain blackens i believe by stealing this air that you cannot touch me even as your knife carves my brain it is a monochrome nightmare plunging into my eyes guided by pale hands i see blood but i need more you gave me an oracle but i need bones show me your hands show me every cracked callus oozing rancid cowardice i am not unfamiliar with their red horror it burns the tongues of one million mothers it sparkles on ten million suburban screens you must swim through it from birth to survive even if you are born with a stone tied to your neck some say faith can wash away that sin but do not ask why some souls never come clean they are too busy clinging to what they have to see what we have lost one look at your face reveals my place a wave of your hand coils fate tighter around my neck but how many faces turn blue before they stop breathing horror is not a ghost story it is a whole world blind and suffocating

Prisoner's Cinema

Mark Morgan, Jr.

from the moment sunlight lifts the shades on my phosphene abduction
my reductionist brain scrutinizes each grain of color for one more piece
of history, immunizes each strain from destruction, perpetuates the
ceaseless primordial mystery carved in every last codon of every last
starving soul. amorphous pools bleed through intrinsic gray canvas in
a hundred hues but forces ruling each ganglion drip lead me down the
everlasting road on which every dead poet and artist has traveled and
reflected. those dejected by unraveled truths know it's hard to cure
selective blindness. i find this enlightening—those frightened by
darkness are first to shut their eyes tight. they succumb to spiraling
false idols forged in confusion from pressurized synaptic ether.
what new gods will arise, defiling their illusion?

A.J. Douglas

A.J. Douglas is a lover of all things fantasy and comedy, especially when they're combined. She loves to write high fantasy elements like magic, far off places, and dragons, blended with modern-esque themes.

She began writing at a young age, starting with fanfiction. Most of her early work still lurks within the bowels of the internet and no, she will not tell you what or where. :) She also dreamed up and wrote her first full novel while pretending to pay attention during high school Spanish class.

A.J. resides in Oakland County with her husband and two rambunctious little boys. She is a member of the Sterling Heights Creative Writers Workshop, sometimes drops in at local author cons/events, and can also be followed on twitter @authorajdouglas.

Not All That Glitters is Faerie Dust

A.J. Douglas

"No way! Are you that guy from the Gif? You know, the falling-out-of-the-tree-with-the-net one?"

"Yup, that's me." Tamil faked a smile, handing the fae his salted caramel mocha latte. Magic Beanz was experiencing its usual midday uptick, as shoppers lured by the aromas of freshly brewed coffee strolled in for their afternoon pick-me-up. Humans, fae, witches, and other magical folks filled the handful of small square tables that lined the front of the shop. More chatted in the sitting area in the mall's hallway. Behind him, a coworker blended another customer's drink, the whir of the blender and sound of crushing ice drowning out the rest of the noise.

His customer's wings buzzed a little faster with excitement. "Woah! I heard you were from around here. That's some funny stuff. Mind if I get a selfie?" His hand went to the back pocket of his skinny jeans for his phone.

Tamil tried not to cringe too hard. That was the third request this week. "Sorry, can't. I'm on the clock."

"Some of us have places to be," the witch next in line grumbled.

"It's cool. Maybe I'll catch you later sometime, bro." The fae tossed a few coins into a tip jar next to the register and fluttered to the door, blowing steam from his cup.

After pouring the witch's extra dark roast with no cream

or sugar, Tamil's manager told him he could take a break. Cell phone in hand, he sank into a lone creaky folding chair, shoved in a corner of Magic Beanz's unorganized storage room, that doubled as the employee break area. A sleeve of plastic lids had been hanging precariously over the edge of a tall shelf for a week, but nobody made any effort to fix it.

He swiped away the lock screen picture of him and his girlfriend, Delinda, to be greeted by a different picture of them on his home screen. His new summer job had thrown off his entire gaming live-stream schedule, and scrolling through Faebook revealed no shortage of comments about it from his viewers. Quiller hasn't been any better. But would it even be the Internet if people weren't complaining about something? Yesterday, he made a post asking for suggestions for fun date ideas. The response was twenty comments asking when he was going to post his next video, a handful of actual ideas, and a few inappropriate ones. As much as he loved being a gamer, the gaming community could be the worst, sometimes.

A text message from Delinda popped up on his screen. "Excited for tonite?"

"Totally!" he responded. Two of their favorite indie bands, Imaginary Dragons and The Beastie Bards were playing at a local summer concert series. They'd both been saving from their respective jobs for weeks in order to score tickets.

"Great. Can u do me a favor b4 leaving the mall? I need shimmer dust from Apothe-faeries 4 the concert. Can u grab me some?"

"Sure thing."

"Ur the best!" she ended it with a line of several kissy emojis.

Rows of glass vials filled with all sorts of powders, tinctures, and concoctions lined the back wall of Apothe-faeries. Ranging from a tonic claiming to instantly cure headaches, to some cloudy pink liquid that could change your eye color. Tamil traced his finger along a shelf of S's. Most of the space was dedicated to many salves for various cuts and burns...Ah! There was the shimmer stuff Delinda wanted. Between shrinking powder and sleeping dust. Except, the vials of shimmer should have come before shrinking. He made sure to double check the label that he grabbed the right kind, and took it to the cashier.

#

"How was your day?" Delinda asked, as she let Tam through the front door of her house.

"It was a total grind. Get it, because I work in a coffee shop."

Delinda groaned, as she pushed the door shut. "Ugh! PLEASE tell me you stole that joke from your dad..."

"Nope, that was all me." He gave her a giant grin.

"Is it too late to break up with you?" She teased, leading him into the kitchen.

"Oh, please, if I didn't dump you after last year's dragon fiasco, then I think you'll survive my awful jokes. Your parents aren't home yet? he asked, looking around.

"Nope. That's how it is every egg-laying season. They've basically been living at the dragon barn all week."

Tamil shuddered. "I think I'm traumatized from baby dragons for life. It took forever for my eyebrows to grow back."

"Did you get my shimmer dust?" Delinda asked, offering her hand.

He reached into the leg pocket of his cargo shorts, removing a small, crinkled brown paper bag and handed it to her.

Delinda pulled the vial from the bag and pursed her lips,

scrutinizing it. "Hmm, did they change something?" She swirled the silver powder around inside the glass. "It's usually gold."

Tamil shrugged. "How should I know. I've never bought it before."

"Whatever, as long as it works." Delinda stepped into the hallway bathroom. She uncorked the vial and dumped its entire contents into her hair, teasing it through her long red curls with her fingers. Puffs of silver powder wafted around her, coating her shoulders and Imaginary Dragons tank top.

Tamil leaned against the wall outside the door, bumping the back of his head on the corner of a family portrait. "Do you have to use the whole thing?" He ducked away, rubbing at the sore spot.

Delinda leaned forward, checking the mirror to make sure her look was just right. "Do you realize how thick my hair is? It takes a whole bottle to get the effect I want. Otherwise, I'll look like I dumped a handful of glitter on my head."

"If you say so." He turned and headed into the kitchen for the sink, helping himself to a glass etched with a dragon scale design from the cupboard. Delinda's parents loved their dragons so much, the whole house had dragon themed everything: glasses, plates, figurines, soap dish... As he filled it, he heard her shout over the running water.

"Tam! We have a big problem!"

He turned toward her, and almost dropped the glass when he saw what was happening. Delinda stood in front of him, getting smaller, and smaller and smaller, until she was the size of one of his childhood toy orc figurines. He stuttered, struggling to find the right words until he finally managed a "What happened?"

"You tell me." She crossed her arms, thrusting her hip to the side. Her voice came out as a high-pitched squeal. "Did you buy the wrong one?"

Tamil covered his mouth with his hand, his body

trembling as he fought to hold in his laugh.

"This isn't funny!" Delinda stomped her foot, putting all of her emphasis into it.

"Yes, it is!" He lost the battle, doubling over as he cackled. He sucked in several deep breaths in an attempt to calm himself down.

Delinda scowled, arms still crossed, as she watched him. "Are you done?" she snapped.

"I think so." Tamil straightened and wiped at his eyes.

"Great! What are we going to do?" She tossed her hands over her head. "I can't go to the concert like this. And my parents are gonna flip if they come home and find their daughter the size of a matchstick!"

"You're a little bigger than a matchstick..." Tamil held his hand up with a gap between his finger and thumb.

"Tam!"

"All right, all right!" he acquiesced. "Here." He bent over, holding his hand to the ground palm up for Delinda to step onto. After setting her on the counter, he walked to the bathroom to retrieve the vial. "Let's figure out what's going on, first," he said, as he re-entered the kitchen. Sure enough, the label read *shimmer dust*. "It says it's the right thing...unless I somehow forgot how to read. See for yourself." He set the vial on the counter next to her.

Delinda inspected it while twirling a long strand of hair around her finger. "This doesn't make any sense... And of course this happens when we have someplace to be! Ugh!" Her voice's already high pitch increased with her frustration.

Tamil had to squeeze his lips together to keep from laughing all over again, earning him an icy glare from his girlfriend. He cleared his throat, keeping himself centered. "Maybe they had a mix-up?" he suggested. "I'm sure they sell a reversal. I'll give them a call, we'll go up there and get it and this will be no big deal." He pulled his phone from his pocket to look up the number for Apothe-faeries.

"They'd better..." Delinda grumbled, scuffing her foot across the counter top. She re-crossed her arms and started to pace.

"Ok, I found it!" Tamil said. He was about to press dial when he heard Delinda's shrill squeal behind him. "What's wrong!" He spun around, fearing the absolute worst: that her cat must have jumped on the counter and thought she was a toy, or snack. Instead, he saw her crouched in front of the toaster.

"Oh, my GOSH, have you seen what it looks like under here? It's full of crumbs and other nastiness! When was the last time anyone moved this thing to clean?" She straightened, swiping her hands to the side as if to wipe the sight away altogether. "I can't even look at it anymore."

Tamil scoffed. "Geez, Lind! I thought something bad happened to you." He turned back to his phone and hit call.

"Hullo?" The bored sounding cashier answered after several rings.

Tamil snatched the bottle from the counter, triple checking that he read the label correctly. "Hi, I was at your store earlier and picked up a bottle of what was supposed to be shimmer dust, except it shrunk my girlfriend."

"Sheesh, not another one..." She sounded irritated, rather than concerned over their predicament. Just how many people did they accidentally shrink today?

"What's that supposed to mean?" Tamil asked.

The fae sighed. "We had a new employee mix up the labels. Our manager can put a reversal on hold for you, free of charge, but we close in fifteen minutes."

He glanced at the dragon-egg-themed wall clock. It was already 5:45 in the evening. The drive to the mall would take at least twenty minutes, even with the off-chance of traffic being on their side. "We can't make it there in fifteen. Is there any way you could stay open maybe five extra minutes? We're kinda in a hurry, ourselves."

"That's not happening."

So much for customer service. Tamil ran his free hand through his dark wavy hair, his mind racing to figure out some way to solve this problem they shouldn't even be having in the first place. "Do you know anyplace else or have any other suggestions."

"The effects of the powder last for twenty-four hours, you could wait it out. Or maybe try Sylph's Solutions in East Haven."

After hanging up with the cashier, he let out an exasperated groan. East Haven was a town that was an hour drive one way. Even if by chance they made it to Sylph's Solutions before it closed, they would be late to their concert. He figured if anything, it could be a backup plan.

Delinda sat on the counter, legs crossed, head resting in her hands. "So, what's the deal? It doesn't sound like things ended well."

"They're closing, so we won't be able to get a reversal from them. The other options are to wait out the powders effects, or try a place an hour from here," Tamil recounted.

"We are NOT waiting for this to wear off!"

"It's only for twenty-four hours. We could still go to the concert. You can sit on my shoulder." Even as he was saying it, the suggestion sounded dumb. There was no way Delinda would ever go for it.

"Tam, are you crazy? What if I fall off and get lost? Or trampled?"

"My shirt has this little pocket." He tugged it open. "I could keep you safe in here."

"No!" She stood and resumed her pacing from earlier. The front of her hair was twisted and disheveled from her twirling it. "We'll try the other place and be late to the concert. I'd rather be late, than miss it altogether."

#

Delinda sat inside the cup holder in Tamil's car, arms splayed, feeling along its smooth rounded sides, desperate for anything to hold onto. Even though he drove as careful as possible, every single start, bump, and turn was exaggerated at her size.

A sudden stop sent her tumbling forward. "What's going on?" she asked, pushing up on her hands and knees, gummy soda residue coating her palms. Delinda scrunched her face, with a silent "Ack."

"I've got an idea," Tamil said, turning into a parking lot. "What if we try a different kind of magic store? That Elixir Sister's place is in this strip mall. Maybe witch magic could do the trick."

Delinda tried to wipe her sticky hands off on her pants, only to get them dirtier with cat hair and lint. "Would that even work?"

Tamil shrugged. "I dunno, but it doesn't hurt to go in and ask."

He set Delinda in his shirt pocket, her head and hands peeping over the top. The smells of patchouli and sandal wood assaulted their senses the moment the shop door dinged. A table covered in bowls full of different rocks and crystals was spread before them. Shelves stocked with candles and books lined an adjacent wall. The rest of the store was dedicated to premade concoctions as well as potion home-brewing supplies.

A middle-age woman in a flowing skirt peered from around an aisle, greeting them.

"Hi, we have a little situation here—" Tamil began to explain.

"Really, Tam?" Delinda shouted at him.

"I didn't mean that as a pun!" He tried his explanation again. "Apothe-faeries sold us shrinking dust instead of shimmer, but they were closing before we could get there for a reversal. Do you happen to have anything that might help?"

The witch shook her head with an eyeroll. "They wouldn't stay open for you? Typical fae. No, we can't help, sorry. Witch magic can't undo fae, and vise versa."

"Do you know of anything else we could try? Otherwise, we'll have to go all the way to East Haven for a different fae store and we have a concert to be at." That long drive was sounding more unappetizing by the minute.

"Sorry, I don't. Wish we could help." Her voice was empathetic as she offered them a smile and excused herself.

As Tamil walked to the door, defeated, someone whispering "Psst," caught his attention. He turned to see a young man beckoning them over behind an aisle on the other side of the store.

"Gotta keep it low, 'cuz ma would curse me into oblivion if she heard this." The young man swiveled his head from side to side, checking that the coast was clear. "I couldn't help but overhear your problem. I know a werewolf across town who sells all sorts of unregulated magical goods." He slipped a business card into Tamil's hand. "Get in touch with him, he'll help you out." He said nothing more, and returned to stocking jarred eye of newt on a shelf.

Once outside, Tamil took a peek at the worn card in his hand. It was blank except for a few printed lines of text. "Nausea? Heart burn? Demon possession? Cursed by a scornful ex? Hex-lax has you covered." And a number for text messages only.

\#

Tamil shut the car off, and leaned back in his seat. "I can't believe we've come to this part of town for black market faerie powder."

"Let's get it over with." Delinda stood, stretching her arms over her head. "We'll still catch most of the opening band if we hurry."

He placed Delinda in his shirt pocket once more, and

exited the car. Across from the gray bricked rundown apartment building, a trio of pale-skinned teens with blood-red eyes, two boys and a girl, watched them. Behind the blond-haired boy on the end was a window for the vacant office, and Tamil couldn't help but notice that the boy had no reflection. "Vampires across the street from a werewolf," he mumbled to Delinda. "I hope we didn't stumble into a turf war."

Delinda tsked. "That stuff is from books and movies. Vampires and werewolves get along fine in real life. My dad trains security dragons for a pair who are business partners."

Next to the door for the apartment building was an intercom. As per instructions in the Hex-lax guy's message, Tamil pressed the grimy button for #308.

After several moments, a male voice crackled and popped over the speaker. "If this is Ronan, for the last time I told you that your wolfsbane will be here tomorrow! Go home, already!"

Tamil glanced down at Delinda, not even sure how to respond. She looked up at him with a shrug. "Uhh, no..." was all he could think to say.

"Oh, you must be that kid for the fae powder. C'mon up!" A faint click came from the front door.

"Wolfsbane? Isn't that dangerous? Why would he be selling it?" Delinda asked as Tamil climbed the stairs.

"I don't know, and I don't think I wanna know why," he replied. The rest of their trip was silent, save for creaks from old, musty stairs and worn floorboards. "Why does it feel like we're doing something wrong?" he mumbled, coming to a stop in front of their destination. Hesitating at first, he reached up and knocked on the door.

A muscular young man with slicked back hair and light brown eyes greeted them with a toothy smile. "Hey, sorry 'bout that wolfsbane comment." He ushered them inside. "My, uh... buddy needs some for a pest problem and us

44

werewolves... we don't have a reputation for our patience. Get what I'm sayin'?" He nudged Tamil with his elbow. "You can call me Alaric, by the way." He leaned in, taking a look at Delinda. "Wow, you weren't kiddin' about your shrinking problem. No worries, I've got just what you need." He turned, walked down the hall, and entered a room on the left, closing the door and leaving them alone.

Tamil glanced around. Alaric's living room was plain, with white walls and only a tan couch and wood coffee table for furniture. The only thing that stood out was a printed canvas of a fully transformed werewolf under a full moon, hung on the wall. The beast stood at least seven feet tall on his hind legs, covered in silver bristly fur. His snout, full of long fangs was open in a silent roar as he smashed through the roof of a car with his fists. Visible through the fur on his right forearm was the same tattoo their host sported.

"Is this your shifted form?" Tamil turned to ask as he heard Alaric approach.

"Yeah!" His face beamed with pride. "Some friends and I tore up a junkyard and one of them caught that picture of the tenth car I destroyed that night. I couldn't not print it."

Tamil made a mental note to never, ever cross a werewolf. He caught the clear, cosmetic sized plastic pot Alaric tossed to him. Inside was a miniscule amount of chalky dark orange powder.

"This will work?" Delinda scrutinized it as Tamil held the jar in front of her. "I wanna be sure, because we were told only fae magic could undo this."

Alaric flopped onto his sofa, propping his sock covered feet on the coffee table. "I've got a trustworthy connection." He stared at his right hand, watching it shift into its werewolf form. He flexed his fingers a few times, light gleaming off enormous shiny black claws. "It's a multi-purpose reversal for fae magic and will do what you need it to. That should be enough to get you back to size. Did you bring the cash?" he asked, buffing one of the claws with the cuff of his shirt sleeve.

Tamil dug out his wallet, and removed the wad of bills. He felt part of his soul leave his body at the amount this was costing them. So much for snacks and a Beastie Bards shirt tonight. At least Delinda promised to split the cost. "This tiny amount is that expensive?" he asked, handing the money over.

"I said it would work, I didn't say it'd be cheap." Alaric didn't bother to look up as he counted the cash. "All right, that'll do it," he said, satisfied with the amount. "Sprinkle on the whole thing and you'll be good to go. I trust you can see yourselves out?"

They couldn't do so fast enough. Tamil made a bee line down the stairs and back outside to his car. "How are we gonna do this?" He asked Delinda as he moved her from his shirt pocket to the cup holder.

"Let's go back to my house. We'll figure out what to do from there."

#

Delinda sat on her kitchen counter as Tamil dug in his pocket for the reversal dust. They both looked up as the ringtone she set for her parents played from the living room.

"Oh, my gosh, my parents!" she gasped and jumped to her feet. "Tam, go grab my phone!"

He rushed to it, but didn't get there before the call went to voicemail. "Hey, Lind, you've got over twenty missed calls," he said, carrying her phone back into the kitchen.

"Oh, no!" She ran her fingers through her hair, grabbing the ends of it. "Why didn't they call you? They knew we had plans this evening. Ugh, my mom has got to be freaking out!"

Tamil cringed. "They might have... I don't think I ever turned my phone off silent after leaving work."

"Are you serious? You have to call my mom right away!"

"And say what?" He asked as he checked his own phone, noticing a dozen missed calls as well. "Why don't we turn you back right now and then you can call."

"Because we don't know how long it will take, or if it will even work. Just call my mom, then we'll use the reversal. And… make something up. If she finds out I got shrunk and we're about to use black market fae powder, she'll flip! Tell her we had a quick errand to run and I forgot my phone."

That wasn't technically a lie. "All right," he caved, dialing Delinda's mom.

"Tam?" her mom answered. "Where have you two been? We've been trying to call you both all afternoon." He could tell she'd been worried.

"Sorry 'bout that. We had to run out to get something for the concert. Delinda forgot her phone and mine was on silent." He started to pace around the kitchen.

"My daughter, forget her phone? She's usually attached to it. Where is she?"

"Uhhh… She's in the bathroom…"

"Oh, okay. Well can you tell her that—" her mom launched into some long message for her daughter about them being late again, which led into her gushing on about baby dragons.

Tamil bounced on the balls of his feet, waiting for a moment to interject and try to end the conversation. But her mom kept talking and talking. Behind him, Delinda screamed. He spun around, ready to tell her to stop fussing over the toaster crumbs and was horrified to see the family cat standing on the counter instead. "Ahhhh! Sorrygottagobye!" He hung up, and leapt for the counter shooing the cat away. But, when he looked, Delinda was nowhere in sight. "Delinda!" he called, searching the counter. There was no trace of her anywhere. He glanced to the kitchen doorway and saw Norbert slink off, twitching his gray plume of a tail.

"Norbert, no!" He dashed after the feline.

The cat startled. His claws scratched the tile as he scurried into the living room and under the sofa.

Tamil belly flopped to the floor between the couch and coffee table, nearly whacking his elbow in the process. "Here, kitty! It's okay, I didn't mean to scare you." He tried to coax Norbert, reaching for him. Norbert responded by hunkering in the corner with a low warning growl. The claws would be coming next. Defeated, Tamil rested his forehead on the floor. Even if he did catch the cat, what would it accomplish? He pushed himself from the ground and made his way back into the kitchen. Maybe in his panic he missed something and she was still hiding. In the back of his mind, he hoped he wouldn't be explaining to Delinda's parents that she got accidentally shrunk and eaten by their cat.

Standing at the counter he composed himself. She had to be here somewhere. He started by checking around and under appliances like the toaster and coffee maker. As he peeked inside a cup hanging on the lowest hook of the coffee mug tree, he heard it. The sound was quiet and difficult to hear, but no doubt it was Delinda's high pitched squeal shouting his name. Tamil froze, wishing his heart would stop beating so darn loud as he tried to zero in on where it was coming from. He took a couple of steps along the counter, coming to a stop in front of the fruit basket. A flash of red caught his attention. There Delinda was, in the fruit bowl, wedged between a pair of bananas.

"Oh, my gosh, there you are!" he said, relief filling him as he leaned over. He was so happy he could almost cry.

"Geez, I didn't think you'd ever find me!" Her voice strained as she struggled to free herself. "I wasn't sure how much longer I'd be able to yell."

Tamil freed her, setting her on the counter. "We are unshrinking you before anything else bad happens." He retrieved the orange powder. Pinching it between his fingers, he sprinkled it over her head.

Nothing happened.

"It's not working?" Delinda fretted. "So help me if this stuff doesn't—" She never got to finish her sentence. In an instant her body sprang back to its normal size so fast, her head almost collided with her boyfriend's face.

Delinda looked at each arm, then her legs, and all the rest of her. She laughed. She was finally back to normal! She flung herself from the counter and into Tamil's arms.

"I was freaking out, thinking you got eaten by your cat," he said as they broke apart.

"I was freaking out, thinking I was about to get eaten by my cat." Delinda breathed a deep sigh. "But at least it's over. And I'm never shopping at Apothe-faeries again. What's wrong?" She looked at him, concerned.

Face buried in his hand, Tamil's shoulders shook as he started to laugh. "You were stuck in the freaking bananas. This whole afternoon... I can't believe how absurd it was."

"That seems to be our luck." Delinda smiled. "It's like we're a magnet for weird things to happen to us." She took his hand and pulled him to the front door. "Now, come on! We have a concert to get to."

Judy Khadra

Judy Khadra, wife, mother, grandmother, grew up in Greenville, Texas. She attended The University of Texas for one year, met and married her husband, a Palestinian. They moved to Syria after his graduation, where they lived for one year.

She is currently working on a memoir from her Syrian experience based on letters she and her family wrote during 1962 to 1963. Her greatest achievements are having accomplished children and grandchildren.

The Lily Pond

Judy Khadra

Nothing would die in that pond, swirling with life,
Eggs hatched into tadpoles looking for water-bugs skating,
Lilies blossomed and grew,
Sending their stems down to root in the depths,
While green glossy pads floated gently on
blue rippled circles.

What myriads of color!

Golden sun-shafts slicing the deeps,
Silver-orange fish, pearly-black snails,
Turtles, bubbles, and snakes danced together in birth.

Nothing would die in this place:
Even the rainbowed oil blobs multiplied daily.

T.L. Patrick

Tim Patrick is an author, business owner, and facilitator of Writers' Rendezvous at the Bloomfield Township Public Library.

His writing has appeared in numerous trade journals, the Oakland Press, and the 2017 Writers' Rendezvous Anthology. His work was a runner-up in the 14th Annual Oakland University Flash Fiction contest. He published a paper in the 2003 Meeting of Minds Journal of Undergraduate Research at the University of Michigan-Dearborn.

Free Fall

T.L. Patrick

Dan "Mad Dog" Edwards watched the rice paddies slip beneath the wings of his F-100 Super Sabre as he raced toward Plei Me in the Central Highlands of Vietnam.

It was early Sunday morning, October 31, 1965— Halloween back in the states. Instead of passing out candy, he was part of an urgent mission to keep an isolated Special Forces base from being overrun by the Viet Cong. Hung from the wings of his plane were 2 ten-foot-long, 120 gallon canisters of napalm. Jellied gasoline.

When released, the tanks would tumble erratically as they fell and blanket an area about seventy-five-hundred square feet long, creating a 3,600-degree river of fire.

Rico, the flight leader, flashed him a thumbs-up sign and dived toward the target. Mad Dog followed. The G-suit compressed around his already tense abdomen as he plunged toward the jungle. Ahead, green tracer rounds arched up from the dense foliage and across his flight path. He leveled off at fifty feet. Several bullets slammed into the plane with a sharp crack.

He squeezed the trigger to release the napalm and pulled back on the control stick for the safety of the sky. The plane lurched left. Mad Dog glanced out the canopy and saw one of the napalm canisters had failed to release. He retarded the throttle and rocked the wings.

The plane jerked right, and the canister fell free. He watched in horror. The Special Forces base camp flash by. A reflection of a bright orange fireball filled the windscreen. His stomach twisted.

The high-pitched screech from the missile lock warning filled the cockpit. "Rico..." was all he had time to yell into the mic before the air-to-air missile slammed into his plane. It bucked violently upward, the canopy shattering. A hurricane of wind pinned him against the seat. The intense heat of the flames from the missile strike licked at the nape of his neck.

He yanked the ejection seat handles and rocketed skyward as a MIG-21 flashed past. No sooner had the parachute opened than the wake turbulence from the MIG collapsed it.

He fought to free himself from the tangle of shroud lines as he tumbled end-over-end toward the ground.

Desperately, he tried to reach his survival knife to cut away the lines and deploy the reserve. The sound of the battle on the ground below crackled around him. He freed his right hand, grabbed the knife, and began slashing. The reserved chute deployed with a loud pop and jerked him straight up. The harness cut into his upper body. The dense jungle rushed to meet him.

#

Mad Dog landed hard on the bedroom floor. He tore at the tangled bedsheets and sweat-soaked pajamas, which clung to him like burnt flesh. He choked down gulps of air. His heart raced out of control. It was useless. Fifty years later and the nightmare still haunted him. Perhaps, it would have been better if he had died that fateful day.

At the Bottom of the Stairs

T.L. Patrick

From a broken picture frame, you stare and smile
at no one, yet everyone
Only I see you, a promise on Kodachrome

You free from the bonds—me alone
buried beneath the weight of failure

I claw at the debris for air,
Memories of what could have been
but were denied

All that remains are the struggles,
fights—distance, and darkness of our isolation
You look out from empty brown eyes
I look into them, and search for a way to rescue you

You pushed me aside
buried beneath the weight of failure

Images of the past reappear in fragments
like random puzzle pieces

Of 3 a.m. visits to the chapel in search of strength
while you and our daughter slept
Of lonely drives down Hoover in pursuit of
answers that refused to yield
Of restless nights awake on the living room floor

You shunned my love
buried me beneath the weight of failure

Time raced by—options ran out
No more hospital receptionist eager to deny me
access to you
I dreaded the day I would tell your parents of my defeat,
And your transfer to the nursing home

Stairs I once bounded down
now hobble me—each a painful memory
And there, where we've always been, you are,
Free from the bonds

At the bottom of the stairs, in a broken picture frame

Amy Laessle-Morgan

Amy Laessle-Morgan is a writer, poet, and Sterling Heights native. She graduated from Oakland University with a Bachelor's Degree in Communication. Her work has also been featured in the 2020 edition of Sterling Script: A Local Author Collection.

When not writing poetry, Amy enjoys music, photography, traveling, and restoring vintage furniture. She also loves spending time with her family and snuggling with her French bulldog, Margot.

Savannah

Amy Laessle-Morgan

walking in shadows of history
rows of houses burst with color
I am amorous of antebellum architecture
a love poem written in cobblestone

surrounded by fountains and old fortunes
bearded trees of Spanish moss hang down
dripping sweet southern charm
like Tupelo honey

a bridal veil of magnolia blossoms
scents the warm breeze,
marries my heart forever
to this seductive city

High Tide

Amy Laessle-Morgan

standing on sandy shores the ocean breathes salty,
crashing waves envelop bare feet
warm sun on exposed shoulders elicits familiar sensations
of thoughts when I am recalling your good-natured smile
nature lends her beauty, healing wounds and lifting spirits

lying down before the tide that is nearing,
an unexpected baptism from dark shadows to light
to wash away the numbness
crystal clear resolutions slip like sand through spread fingers

if only I could walk again through this moment
clutching hindsight and foresight
equipped with the knowledge and answers
of which path to stroll down

I would have known to tread lightly
leaving only water-flooded footprints
still never forgetting the moonlight and softness,
how they all came together
the pull of the ocean lives forever in my soul

Katy Hojnacki

Katy Hojnacki works with paintings, illustrations, novels, short stories, and even comics to delve into fantasy worlds. She is a writer, avid gamer, artist, and illustrator of the children's book *I Can See With My Eyes Shut Tight*. As cover designer and artist for *Sterling Script: A Local Author Collection*, she also contributes her writing and editorial skills to the publication.

A graduate of Oakland University with a degree in English and Studio Art, Katy is an active member of the Sterling Heights Creative Writers Workshop as well as the Tuesday Morning Writers.

#Stream

Katy Hojnacki

You settle into your creaking computer chair. The monitor flickers to life, and the keyboard crackles as you input your password and log in. The browser cannot boot up fast enough. The time reads 6:58 PM

"Your desk is a mess," says your girlfriend, nudging your elbow. The motion jostles your mouse-hand and sends the cursor sailing to the wrong icon. You open a word processor instead of the Internet.

"I'll clean it after," you say with a sigh. "He starts streaming every day at seven. I don't want to miss it." The hutch over your desk is, arguably, cluttered with Star Wars paraphernalia. The character figures and ships used to be neatly presented, but dust and junk mail have staked their claims.

She rolls her eyes at you with an affectionate, yet scolding look. Nonetheless, she moves a pile of clean clothes off a chair and pulls it next to yours. Removing her pet store name tag, she sets it on the desk next to your discarded ID and keys. Her silky hair falls over her face as her attention turns to the touch-screen tablet on her lap.

You close the empty document and open the correct program. The address bar autocompletes your destination, and the video loads just in time.

"Good evening, you beautiful bastards," says a young man

with a grin. The white of his teeth stands out against the dark olive of his skin. The majority of the screen displays an otherworldly, red landscape with a sea of stars overhead, but the host's face takes up a corner of the video. "SmartyFish360 coming at you live with some more *Deimos 3000* gameplay. Quick thanks to all you supporters who donate to me so I can keep doing this for a living. And you with the ad blocker…I hope you fall into a ditch." He laughs loudly, and the sound quality distorts for a moment. "Just kidding, I love you all. I don't like to ramble, though," he says, adjusting his headphones and brushing a stray black curl from his face, "so let's just get started. Hope you Smarties are all ready for some sweet lasers."

Alongside the video, which now portrays the cockpit of a spaceship, a barrage of names begin sharing their "hellos" and "heys" in the chat section. The listed number of viewers climbs from "50" to "500" in seconds. SmartyFish360 adopts a focused expression as his game begins, but occasionally his brown eyes flicker to the right, and he cracks a smile.

"Hey, Grizmo," he says between clicks. "Hi, Blue Raven. How's school going, bro?"

The messages in the chat sweep past your eyes. Only a few stick out, much in the way a few stray conversations catch in your ear when you pass through a noisy crowd. While SmartyFish360 can fly around in space shooting Martians and talk to six-hundred-some people at the same time, you can hardly catch up with the chat and type your own greeting.

> **Red2_Antilles:** Greetings, fellow
> Smarties!
> **LaraL4rk:** Red2! ♥ Missed you
> **BlueRavenGames:** ayyyy antilles
> **Grizmo:** Hey Wedge

You can't help but smile as Grizmo catches the reference

in your username, as he always does. You appreciate a fellow Star Wars fan.

"Red leader to Red 2!" SmartyFish says with a laugh, greeting you when he turns back to his game. "Hey, man."

Amidst the commentary on SmartyFish's space adventures, the chat carries on. Like regulars in a bar, familiar names in the chat play catch up. LaraL4rk is trying to teach English to her new boyfriend, Yvgeny. Grizmo, as always, functions on too little sleep, and BlueRavenGames struggles with algebra homework. You help him solve a few equations. At least your math degree went to some use.

A series of foul messages flash in the chat before changing to [message deleted; user banned]. A hammer icon appears next to Grizmo's name.

> **Grizmo:** Keep your racist garbage out of here.
> **BlueRavenGames:** Griz banhammer!!!!
> **Red2_Antilles:** There's always a troll.
> **LaraL4rk:** They know he's american, right? Lol
> **Grizmo:** I'm so done with this shit today.

You enjoy the stream for a few hours, breaking only to reheat some leftovers with your girlfriend. She sets aside her tablet, and the two of you relax to the live stream. She coos when SmartyFish's bright orange cat sashays across the back of the young man's chair. Leaning on your shoulder, she insists you ask its name. Smarty laughs and tells you the cat is called Sweet Potato.

A low boom echoes in the background. Sweet Potato springs from Smarty's chair, and the gamer's head snaps to look behind him. You exchange a look with your girlfriend, who frowns. The chat becomes alight with messages: what was that? Was that the game? Is your cat okay?

SmartyFish, brow furrowed, turns back to his game and mutters, "Probably nothing." The image of his face flickers to darkness, but returns. He continues to play, but he glances to his right. "Yes, chat, I heard it. Don't worry about it, okay?"

The streamer's eyes widen as a loud crash interrupts his playing once more. Turning to look behind him, he sighs heavily. He takes off his headphones, and they lightly clatter on the desk as he sets them down. A few minutes pass, during which the video shows nothing but the *Deimos 3000* pause menu and SmartyFish's empty chair. The screen cuts to black, then displays the familiar "The stream is over! Thanks for watching, Smarties!" message, like credits to a movie.

"I guess he's ending early today," you say as your girlfriend rises from her chair. You sort the mail on your desk, setting most of it in the recycling pile. You wipe the dust from your shelves with a dirty sock and set your figures back into place.

#

The clock reads 7:24 PM, and the SmartyFish360 stream still has not begun. After a long day of too many customers with expired coupons, you just want to watch someone blast aliens on the Martian plain. *Jeopardy* wouldn't get away with being half an hour late, you think bitterly, then chide yourself for holding a nineteen-year-old kid to the same standards as a 50-year-running game show.

"Let's just watch a movie," suggests your girlfriend. You wave her off. You refresh SmartyFish's Twitter feed in case he's posted an update there.

At 7:32 PM, you receive the notification that the stream is live. Thirty-two minutes late.

"Good evening, you beautiful bastards," comes the familiar greeting. Smarty flashes a smile to the camera, but you notice the tired look in his eyes. "Sorry about the late start—let's get right to some Martian ass-kicking, am I right?"

The ambient, futuristic soundtrack of *Deimos 3000* rumbles through your speakers, rattling a few loose pens on your desk. Turning the volume down, your girlfriend gives you a look, which you ignore. She settles back in her chair to observe the flashing lights and vast Martian landscape on screen. Snatching the keyboard, you type your typical greeting into chat before it gets too crowded.

```
Frogsaregood99: first
poptropica: first
poptropica: dang it
Red2_Antilles: Greetings, fellow
Smarties!
Grizmo: Hey.
wackywerewolf: ur late
Chimmy88: Hoi!!
Johnderoo: hey stream
wackywerewolf: what happened last night
Frogsaregood99: Yo @SmartyFish360 you
should try the laser shotty today
```

"Laser shotty..." says SmartyFish when you see his gaze wander off-center. "Oh, you mean the Polaris shotgun? I could give **that a tr**y, Frogs." The audio briefly warps low on SmartyFish's voice.

With the stream starting later, SmartyFish's webcam background is darker than usual. The shadows on his face run deep, and despite the gamer's monitor reflecting Martian red, his brown skin looks cold and pale.

```
wackywerewolf: hey
wackywerewolf: hey
wackywerewolf: what happened last night
wackywerewolf: @SmartyFish360
Grizmo: he's reading chat already
```

> **Red2_Antilles:** Glad you're back today,
> Smarty! I was worried
> **Johnderoo:** people still play deimos?
> **LaraL4rk:** Smarty would never leave us
> hanging ♥

The rhythmic *pings* form a short melody while SmartyFish360 chooses his weapon in the game: indeed the laser gun someone recommended. Whatever the streamer says next is too distorted by his microphone to understand as he starts his match, and the only audio playing is the thump of his character's boots on the Martian soil. SmartyFish's mouth continues to move as though he is speaking.

> **Frogsaregood99:** yee! laser shotty 4 lyfe
> **Johnderoo:** audio's borked
> **BillT6748:** oof
> **BillT6748:** you look tired as hell dude
> **poptropica:** mute??
> **Grizmo:** Carlos, fix your mic.
> **wackywerewolf:** why is no one answering me
> **wackywerewolf:** u look like u got beat up
> **wackywerewolf:** @SmartyFish360
> **Red2_Antilles:** Yeah, your voice is off

"Lot of stream problems lately, huh?" says your girlfriend, watching as SmartyFish clicks off the game. In game, his astronaut character stands and twirls the shotgun in his hands.

"Apparently," you say, adjusting the volume down again as the streamer's voice becomes an eerie rumble. Once the error is remedied, Smarty goes on with the stream, complete with chat confirmation that the sound is back to normal. The laser shotgun provides a particularly satisfying spray of colors, which your girlfriend finds far more entertaining to watch than Smarty's usual loadout.

```
wackywerewolf: @SmartyFish360
wackywerewolf: WHAT
wackywerewolf: HAPPENED
wackywerewolf: LAST
wackywerewolf: NIGHT
Chimmy88: pls don't spam <:3
BillT6748: was wondering about that, you
ok?
poptropica: no he's dead obv cmon people
Grizmo: Just enjoy the stream, guys.
C0c0NUTZ: YOU SUCK
C0c0NUTZ: [message deleted; user banned]
BlueRavenGames: sry i'm late all, hi
```

"Okay, seriously," says SmartyFish360 as his dark eyes turn to the webcam, "Mods, if one more person asks about yesterday, just ban them, okay?" The young man pauses his gameplay to adjust his headphones before his foul look fades to a focused expression. The chat's protests die down (thanks to aggressive message deletion from Grizmo), but you swear there's still something wrong with the audio. Behind the game sounds and SmartyFish's voice, you hear a faint, rambling whisper.

#

Graveyard shifts always drag. With no one to keep you company but the buzzing fluorescent lights, you idly scroll on your phone. Pictures and comments slide in and out of your gaze, as forgettable as the customers at your convenience store.

At 3 AM, your phone buzzes with a notification.

SmartyFish360 is live: Deimos 3000 / Martian Mayhem & S+ Ranked Play

Out of habit, you tap the notification. The stream might drain your data, but you can deal with that at the end of the month.

As SmartyFish360's usual energetic greeting screams from your phone, you quickly slide the volume control down. No one else is in the store, but the echoing sound reminds you that your phone shouldn't be out at work regardless.

"How're you all doing tonight?" SmartyFish says at a more reasonable volume as his face appears in the corner of our screen. "Man, I just got this urge to stream and couldn't resist booting up. Sorry, webcam took a minute. Let's get in here!" The familiar melody of his menu selection brings a sense of serenity to your otherwise eerie store. You type in chat then prop your phone against the register.

> **Red2_Antilles:** My turn to work and lurk!
> **LaraL4rk:** Good morning, Smarty! <3
> **Grizmo:** Late stream... Can't sleep, Carlos?
> **Grizmo:** Me neither.
> **LaraL4rk:** Wow it's like lunchtime here

Despite the late hour, SmartyFish immediately finds fellow players to start a game, some of which have usernames in languages you cannot read. Their characters in the match move oddly, teleporting from place to place as the game tries to adjudicate actions between SmartyFish's American computer and his Russian and Japanese opponents.

> **Moorishwombat:** omg the LAG
> **Grizmo:** damn, idk how you can land any shots on those guys
> **LaraL4rk:** Smarty is such a good sport
> **LaraL4rk:** Most people just whine about the connection

The chime of the door spooks you. Immediately, you flop your phone onto its face and lock its screen. You force a smile at the new customer, who doesn't so much as look at you until he dumps four bags of chips and a Pepsi on the counter. After you ring up his order, you watch him shuffle as slowly as possible out the door so that you can pull your phone out again.

You turn the volume back up and squint at the poor quality video.

"And that'll be all tonight, folks!" says the streamer. "Catch you tomorrow at the normal time for more Martian massacres!"

> **Moorishwombat:** welp guess that's all we get
> **Grizmo:** Go to bed, dude.
> **Red2_Antilles:** Boo :(Missed the match for a customer
> **LaraL4rk:** Sweet dreams, America!

Disappointment sinks your stomach as you realize you will be left alone in the store again as you watch the stream wrap up. The brown skin on SmartyFish's jaw and neck is stained a bluish purple. You only have a few seconds to look before his outro screen flashes.

"What the hell?" you mutter, making a note to check the video archive later. You should probably do inventory before your boss gets to work in a few hours anyway.

#

It's 6:00 PM There is an hour before SmartyFish360's next stream, so your girlfriend focuses on having dinner ready in time. Your eyes glaze as you comb over last night's stream frame-by-frame. You only missed a few minutes while that

71

customer was in the store, and no matter how many times you go over the footage, the bruises on the streamer's neck seem to appear over just a few frames.

"Did you see Smarty's stream the other night?" You look to the kitchen. The rhythmic thud of the knife on the cutting board ceases.

"I don't watch him when you're not here," your girlfriend calls back over the sizzle of the frying pan.

"He started streaming at three in the morning, and it... was really weird," you say.

"More technical trouble?"

"No, more like..." You play the clip forward and backward, watching the marks appear and disappear. "...Scary."

"Scary? Is he playing a spooky game now?"

"No, not the game, *him*. I've been looking over the stream archives. Last night, he had a bruise appear out of nowhere. The one before has this whispering sound... I gotta download the file and see if I can isolate the audio," you say, navigating to SmartyFish360's channel. "Something's going on. What if he's getting abused or something?"

"Is this all over that stream he cut off?" says your girlfriend, rolling her eyes. "He probably just got swatted or something. If he talks about it, people will get ideas and call the cops."

"No, I don't think so," you say, mostly to yourself. Saving the clip, you make a new folder and start compiling your evidence. Maybe if you had others looking out for anything shady going on during SmartyFish360's stream, you could let this go. If something awful *is* going on, bringing awareness to it might help in the end.

"Dinner's ready," your girlfriend calls from the kitchen.

"Yeah, one minute," you say, pulling up Twitter.

Red Squadron #2 @red2_antilles 1m
I don't want to freak anyone out, but
@SmartyFish360 might be in danger. Some weird
stuff going on in his #Deimos3000 streams lately.
Keep an eye out and DM me if you see anything
besides what's here...
#SaveSmarty

In the replies, you add your evidence. Screenshots of the bruises. The slowed down clip of the marks appearing. An audio clip of the strange mumbling in the background.

You hit send just in time to join your girlfriend for her last few bites. Her look is as cold as your dinner. You ignore the pings on your phone as you enjoy her cooking and make the executive decision that you can be late to SmartyFish360's stream today.

When you do tune in, you notice the viewer count is higher than usual as SmartyFish finishes up another match in *Deimos 3000*. His character does a showy pose with a new laser pistol.

Red2_Antilles: Sorry I'm late! STREAM
HYPE!
LaraL4rk: Hey Red!
LaraL4rk: gg Smarty!
Hearability: I used to play Deimos 3000
ages ago!
Sp00nz: dead game lul
KobayashiMaru_: gg
Thebritishnerd: gg
Xonten: cat cat cat cat look at the cat
Grizmo: Another day, another rank up.
Nicely done.

"Whoo! That was a tough match. Catchin' all those GG's in chat, thanks, guys!" The young man on screen sighs in relief as he leans back in his chair. The bright orange cat perched on his headrest digs its claws in. Fur bristled, it hisses at something behind the chair. The shadows catch on the streamer's brown-skinned face until he sits back up into the better lighting. "Damn, hello, view count! There's a lot of you in here! If you're new, don't forget to drop that follow so we can hang out whenever I'm streaming."

> **Sp00nz:** only one still playing deimos lolz
> **Oddity:** What is the cat looking at?
> **BlueRavenGames:** dude that was awesome, you should main that pistol
> **Funchucker:** stream sucks not one ghost
> **Red2_Antilles:** OMG! Did he just hit X Rank? That's awesome!
> **Sp00nz:** d e a d g a m e
> **Grizmo:** @Red2_Antilles, DM me after stream.
> **Grizmo:** Sp00nz, bro, stop or you're banned.

You flinch for a moment as Grizmo calls you out in chat. Why would a moderator want to talk to you? You just got to the stream. Unless he wants help with the stream chat? You've never moderated a stream before, but you pay enough attention to chat that you could probably help out, given there's twice as many viewers as usual.

Sweet Potato, the cat, hisses and leaps off Smarty's chair. Your girlfriend pouts as the cat leaves the frame, her primary motivation for watching now lost. She elbows you and glares at your phone, which is still dinging with new messages.

The streamer gives his pet a confused look, shakes his

head and turns back to his game just in time for it to crash. The video game screen goes black. SmartyFish sighs heavily. His frustrated clicks pick up on the microphone during the silence. You think you see a wall of dark red text scroll over the screen before he boots the game back up.

"Damn, not again," he says. "Sorry, guys. This game just does not want to cooperate today."

> **Sp00nz:** FAKE
> **C0c0NUTZ2:** just doing it for views
> **wackywerewolf:** who are all these people
> **DeadmansJest:** did anyone screenshot that
> **CobrasAreHot:** boring I'm out
> **LaraL4rk:** perk up, Smarty!! It'll work this time <3

Your phone continues to beep. Tearing your eyes away from the constant stream of chat, you finally notice the dozens of Twitter notifications piling up on your phone.

Your Twitter thread is exploding. You can hardly parse the volume of comments, so you go to the Tweet and scroll through it like you would someone *else's* viral post. Several users immediately latch onto Smarty's peril and repost to signal boost the message. The more interesting replies are clips and screenshots—clips you don't recognize.

You turn down the volume on SmartyFish's live video while you investigate the new evidence. A freeze frame of Smarty's webcam feed background shows his front door, locked shut with several heavy chains. Several more clips of warped audio slow the footage down and try to put subtitles to a strange, deep voice speaking underneath the streamer's chipper tone. Someone has clipped the most recent *Deimos 3000* game crash, noting that a few of the dark red symbols on the unusual screen looked like alchemical notations.

In the meantime, SmartyFish360 has gotten his game

working again. While the match connects with the other players, he tries to lure Sweet Potato on camera with one of the Goldfish crackers he was snacking on. The cat audibly hisses before the mic picks up its thumping footsteps darting out of the room.

> **LaraL4rk:** Oh no!!! Sweetie baby, come back!!
> **DeadmansJest:** Cat saw somethin
> **C0c0NUTZ2:** ghost stories fake smh, maybe if you didn't play like trash you'd have real views
> **Xonten:** SCARED CAT AWAY, UNSUBSCRIBE
> **Sp00nz:** *[message deleted, user banned]*
> **Grizmo:** I do not bluff when it comes to bans, buddy.
> **BlueRavenGames:** finally! bye bye

Despite the antagonistic chat, SmartyFish360's view count is higher than you've ever seen it. His on-screen alerts for new people following his channel or giving small donations are happening so frequently, they overlap each other.

"Dang, thanks for all the follows and donations! You're not even giving me enough time to shout you all out," says Smarty. "Hey, Blue, you want to be a mod? We've got a bunch of new peeps here tonight…"

Your heart sinks a little. Maybe if you'd been more active in chat instead of sleuthing, you might be the one who could flex on some of the trolls. As BlueRavenGames excitedly agrees, you see the icon appear next to his name that indicates his new status as a moderator.

Shaking your head, you tab back to Twitter. Out of the corner of your eye, you notice that #SaveSmarty is somehow *trending*. On top of that, you have a few direct messages. Two are from people whose names you don't recognize, but one is

76

from Grizmo. You click on his message.

@grizmothegr8
What the hell, Red? Why are you
posting all this shit on twitter?

@red2_antilles
What do you mean?

@grizmothegr8
You know what I mean. This is going
to give Carlos so much unwanted
attention. We've got a storm of
trolls coming in.

@red2_antilles
Do you not see all the weird stuff that's been
going on? I think it's worth the trolls if Smarty's
in trouble. Besides, he's getting a ton of views
and donations right now. It'll balance out.

@grizmothegr8
Yeah, like the $666 from "BaPHoMetIsBae"
is a real donation. Come on. Do you know
how much Streamers get charged when
someone refunds a PayPal donation?

@red2_antilles
I didn't think about that. Sorry.
But you've gotta admit there's some weird
stuff going on. I'm really concerned.

@grizmothegr8
If he was in trouble, I'd know. Please keep
your fucking conspiracy off of Twitter.

Shaking, you look away from Grizmo's DMs. A fire stirs in your chest as you hit the BLOCK button and tab back to the stream. Did he really think you were making this up? If that was the case, why would there be so many clips and screenshots from so many people if you were the only one who thought something suspicious was happening?

You take a deep breath and try to just watch the stream. The familiar soundtrack from *Deimos 3000* and SmartyFish's voice take your mind off of Twitter. The streamer loudly crunches handfuls of Goldfish crackers until the chat protests en masse to the sound.

Laughing, Smarty mutes his microphone until he finishes chewing. "Oh, my god. Sorry, guys," he says. A deep shadow passes over his brown-skinned face as he leans to set the orange package off-camera. His voice drops in pitch in the middle of his chatter. "Look, we h**ave to make some sacrifices if** I'm going to land that Goldfish sponsorship. The branding is *too* perfect. Please, if anyone out there works for Pepperidge Farm, I'm begging you. Business email's in the description." He gives the webcam a cheeky grin.

The stream's view count is still exploding. You watch the numbers tick up, hovering at nearly a million active viewers. You can still skim the chat, but not read the messages in their quick succession. That is, until a barrage of users, probably from Twitter, begin to repeat the same message in chat, digitally chanting like a crowd at a protest.

> **KobayashiMaru:** #SaveSmarty
> **marshmellow420:** #SaveSmarty
> **Thebritishnerd:** #SaveSmarty
> **Moorishwombat:** #SaveSmarty
> **ManCobra:** #SaveSmarty
> **anonymous389:** #SaveSmarty
> **Funchucker:** #SaveSmarty
> **babydoll1358:** #SaveSmarty

> **SteamyGiraffes:** #SaveSmarty
> **Xiggy1988:** #SaveSmarty
> **HawkeyeMission:** #SaveSmarty
> **Grizmo:** WHY
> **BlueRavenGames:** Heck
> **BlueRavenGames:** @Grizmo where's the timeout button

As quickly as they came in, the usernames and their hashtag begin to disappear. While the mods are distracted removing the horde, the later arrivals use the opportunity to get the streamer's attention.

> **LilyValley:** @SmartyFish360 We're so worried about you!!
> **angelcakez44:** @SmartyFish360 srsly if u need help just ask
> **LaraL4rk:** Lol? What is happening?
> **SilverSamuRAI:** @SmartyFish360 jump 3 times if you're in danger
> **SilverSamuRAI:** like irl
> **LilyValley:** #Jump3Times #SaveSmarty
> **Grizmo:** AAAAAAAAAARGH

The streamer glances away from his game. His dark eyes skim the chat, and the young man visibly flinches at the odd conversations. Grimacing, SmartyFish360 turns back to the game. He quickly mutes his mic before grabbing another handful of orange crackers to toss into his mouth. A flash of white light on his screen reflects on his face as he chews silently, and the tired shadows under his eyes look deeper than before. How long has this stream been going, anyway?

You look at the clock and realize that your next graveyard shift at work starts in thirty minutes. Despite the flare of panic, you can't bring yourself to look away from the screen and the stream. SmartyFish360's movement is unusual. Normally, his armed astronaut character sprints forward into combat, but now he was specifically taking a side route and exploring more of the Martian terrain.

Jump, jump, jump. Laser shotgun blast. Jump, jump, jump.

> **Grizmo:** Uh. Carlos?
> **SilverSamuRAI:** OMG #SAVESMARTY
> **angelcakez44:** OH NO SMARTY :O
> **LaraL4rk:** Okay now I am worrying
> **BarlBagel42:** dude triple jumps are suboptimal. double jump and mash sprint on landing if you want to actually go fast.

SmartyFish360's microphone remains on mute. The dark-eyed streamer glances over his shoulder and rapidly turns back to the game. A few rogue clicks fire his character's shotgun at no enemies while he glances at the chat, but masks his reaction with another fist full of crackers. The brief distraction results in an enemy character's shots draining his health from full to zero in a few quick bursts.

> **Sp00nzReturnz:** god is this shit still going on? lol get rekt
> **MAXbronzer:** where does he live? someone call police #savesmarty
> **Xonten:** Arizona
> **CobrasAreHot:** he's in phoenix i think
> **C0c0NUTZ3:** can't believe you'd FAKE being in trouble to scare people i used to like your channel
> **SilverSamuRAI:** Call ARIZONA POLICE PLEASE
> **Grizmo:** Mod squad is on it. Please don't dox the streamer...

Fixated on the screen, you watch Smarty's webcam footage in the corner. The lighting in his room is poor given the late hour, but you are more concerned by the strained look on his face and the way his eyes keep darting off screen. His rigid posture indicates intense focus, but the game shows his character idly adjusting his space suit while respawning.

The video window freezes. A white circle of dots spins in the center of the paused video. Frantically, you flail your mouse cursor over the video to check if you accidentally paused the stream. The **LIVE** indicator is grayed out, so you click the refresh button and try again.

> **BlueRavenGames:** oh heck is the stream dead for anyone else?
> **LilyValley:** SMARTY?!
> **DeadmansJest:** dead stream
> **KobayashiMaru:** RIP stream
> **Grizmo:** His internet probably went out. Don't panic.
> **Sp00nzReturnz:** lol dc so ur rank doesnt drop i see how it is
> **SilverSamuRAI:** I AM CALLING 911 RIGHT NOW

You wait, tapping the refresh button on the browser a few more times. The stream video remains black until the website finally recognizes the feed has ended. *SmartyFish360 is offline.*

The clock provides a stern reminder that your shift at work started fifteen minutes ago. If you leave now, you might get away with an excuse, oversleeping or something, but you can't shake the pit of worry in your stomach. Your phone buzzes with notifications from Twitter, though the new posts on the #SaveSmarty hashtag only bring more questions, no answers.

You stir in your desk chair and decide to open a new tab. Clicking into the search bar, you type *how to hack a webcam.*

After an hour of frenzied googling, you download a series of sketchy software programs. Cringing at the explicit ads, you reassure yourself that your anti-virus can clean it up later. You hastily navigate through the programs' interfaces and dig up SmartyFish360's IP address with surprising ease after a two-minute video tutorial.

Finally, you get a video feed. You flinch in surprise, knocking your phone and keys to the floor. Hoping you didn't wake your girlfriend, you glance nervously at the closed bedroom door before leaning towards your computer screen to investigate your find.

The faint light of the webcam provides little detail for the empty room, but you can make out the shape of Smarty's high-backed computer chair and the slumped form of the streamer himself. He leans back in the chair, eyes closed. As his chest rises and falls, a shiver runs down your spine as you realize just how creepy it is that you're watching him sleep. Maybe he just fell asleep after playing for too long and bumped the power cord of his computer long enough to cut the stream. Relieved to see that he is all right, you decide you've done more than enough and go to close the window.

Something bumps the mouse of SmartyFish360's computer. The awakened monitor brightens the webcam feed, and you see a form dart onto the back of the computer chair. Sweet Potato, maybe? Smiling, you hold off on closing the window to get a peek at the cat.

The figure that crawls over his shoulder is too large to be Sweet Potato. The monitor light glistens on wet, greenish scales. A long, rat-like tail drapes over Smarty's shoulder. Crinkled, leathery wings stretch and fold back into place as the creature settles. Its face is flat, with human-like eyes. Bearing a grin with elongated teeth, it turns its head to look directly at the webcam.

You freeze in pure, instinctual fear. You know it can't see you. The webcam is one way. But its penetrating gaze feels like it can see directly through the camera, through the wires, and through the windows on your desktop. Your sweat-slicked fingers slip on the mouse button as you close out of every program on your computer. You shut down the machine.

Sunken City

Katy Hojnacki

Susan Dudgeon

Susan Dudgeon has written stories since she was a little girl. As an adult, she likes to observe people, situations, and family; add a little imagination; pepper with her own opinion; and voilà—she's created a short story. "I've been writing and telling stories all my life," Susan says. "To see it come to fruition is a dream come true. I just want people to read my stories and nod their head or smile."

Susan has lived in Shelby Township for the last four years. For the thirty years prior, she had a small horse farm. Horses and their people gave her a lot of inspiration. "Oh, horse people."

She is now retired from the family business. She has met her soul mate. His name is Georgie. He is a sweet, pain in the dupa, five-pound Yorkie. He has her heart.

Her Enchanted Bedroom

Susan Dudgeon

The first Christmas I went into her room, I just stood in the middle of the hardwood floor. I turned in a circle, like a kaleidoscope, seeing all the unique things.

It was beautiful. Soft pastel colors, lampshades with dangling amber crystals, piles of books stacked on either side of her wooden rocker amongst her vintage furniture. The fragrance of lilacs filled the air.

Her room felt calm and peaceful. It felt safe. It felt like her. For days after Christmas, I would daydream about her room.

Each Christmas, I became more curious and braver. I started looking in her trinket boxes. I found a pocketknife, not the one she always carried; her Grandmother's wedding ring; a P.O.W. bracelet from the Vietnam War; and strands of her favorite horse Cody's tail.

I looked in her nightstand drawer. I found a small handgun wrapped in a man's silk kerchief and a baggie of marijuana.

In a corner of her room was a short stack of light blue hat boxes, filled with cards and letters.

I wanted to just sit down and read the secrets of her life.

I shouldn't. I knew it wasn't right. I lifted the dusty lid off the first box. Right there, on top, was an old Christmas card signed, "Couldn't love you more, Finn."

Finn? Finn who cut wood from the farm's forest all my life?! I knew it! She always denied it when I asked her if Finn was her boyfriend. She always denied it!

Shuffled footsteps sounded in the hallway. Someone is coming. I tried to put the envelope back in the hat box. I dropped it. The floor planks creaked. I crammed the envelope under my sweater and walked out of her room. Right into Aunt Sarah.

"Hey, Liv. What 'cha doin? Plundering through my stuff?" she asked as she touched my cheek.

Feeling caught, I stumbled with the truth. "Ahh...yeah."

"Find anything juicy?" she asked with her eyebrows raised and a laugh. "How old are you now? Twenty, yes, you're twenty. Did you drive here?"

"No. I came with my parents," I answered.

"Perfect. Go pour us a brandy and come sit with me by the fire in the living room."

"I can have a drink?" I asked, not being accustomed to being treated like an adult.

"You're not drinking. You are having a brandy and conversation with your aunt. Take this as a lesson in social graces. Just because you are having a drink doesn't mean you're going to get drunk. One can have a lovely social drink and simply feel the warmth. There is a big difference in feeling toasty and getting toasted."

Aunt Sarah had a special antique brandy decanter with a raised horse head on its side and a pewter stopper. She kept two snifters on a small, oval silver tray. I poured us each a drink.

I still had the card under my sweater. How am I going to get it back in the hat box? Aunt Sarah's long-time words rang in my ear. "The truth is always the answer."

I walked over to the sofa in front of the fire, handed Aunt Sarah her brandy. And the card.

She took both from my hands. A soft smile crept over her

face. "This is from Finn. I miss him. He was a good man." She sipped her brandy. "Show me where you found this." She took my hand and her drink and walked us into her room.

"Right here, Aunt Sarah. In your hat box."

"I've forgotten what I've stuffed where." She took the hat box and sat on the edge of her bed. She fingered through it like she had never seen the contents. I crawled up on the bed next to her.

"Read this one." Laughing, she handed it to me. "I didn't look in your underwear drawer. Love ya. Finn."

Not understanding, I looked at her and scrunched my face. "What?"

"It was a running joke between us. I'd ask him to do some chores around here. He'd just come when he came. It didn't matter if I were home or not. If he'd been in the house, he'd always leave a note. I would tell him, 'I don't care if you're in the house or eat my food, just let the dog out and don't go in my underwear drawer.' He'd laugh and say, 'Already did. Nice thong.'"

I was laughing so hard, tears were rolling down my cheeks. Aunt Sarah always had the best stories. I am pretty sure she exaggerated a little

I took a drink of the brandy. My chest immediately set on fire. It took my breath away.

Aunt Sarah saw the panic in my face. "You'll be all right. Breathe through your nose. You have to sip it."

It was a long minute, but it felt good.

"I remember one of your boyfriends," I stated.

"There's been a few. Two husbands. You don't get to be seventy-five and not have some stories, Liv," she said with no apology.

"What about Finn? He wrote, "Couldn't love you more." Was he one?" I questioned.

She answered in a far away, gentle voice, "Finn was better than a boyfriend. He was my true friend. I loved him. He loved me. That simple." Changing the subject, she asked me, "Do you like this room, Livvie?" Without waiting for an answer, she continued, "It's full of my favorite things."

"I love this room. I have to admit, every Christmas I sneak in here and look through your things. But not your underwear drawer like Finn!" I teased.

"I know you do," Sarah said with a soft chuckle. "If you think something is beautiful, I want you to have it."

I walked over to her vanity and picked up an old Avon bottle. It was a young woman wearing a pink dress cradling a cat. I had wanted this since I was thirteen years old.

"I bought that years ago at the Farmer's Market. It just said 'Olivia' to me. Once I got it home, I thought, she's too young to want this. So, I put it with the rest of my perfume bottles. Here it sits, waiting for you."

She handed me the decanter and kissed my forehead. Her lips moved against my hair, "Merry Christmas, sweetheart. I love you." Her eyes held mine for a second. "Now, c'mon. Let's finish our brandy and get back to the party."

No one even noticed we were gone. The night grew short. It was time to leave. "Good night! Thank you! Drive safe! Love you! Merry Christmas!" We called back and forth across the driveway.

I hugged Aunt Sarah. She looked tired. She hugged me back and kissed the side of my face. "Thank you, Liv. You made my Christmas." Then she hugged me tighter.

Jeff Imber

Jeffrey Imber views his life as a three-act play.

Act One: Jeff plays a psychologist. He is founder of New Directions Counseling Center, hosts a daily radio show, and does PhD research on "Psycho-spiritual Transformation." He and his professional staff help people to heal, change, grow. Consequently, Jeff heals, changes, grows.

Intermission: Recovery, Reinvention

Act Two: Jeff plays a retirement planner. He is founder of Imber Wealth Advisors, Inc., an investment advisory firm. He and his team develop "Retirement Roadmap 360," a holistic technology that brings clarity and structure to investment and retirement planning. IWA helps people design custom plans to enjoy their retirement dreams. Consequently, Jeff applies "Retirement Roadmap 360" to his investments and retirement plan.

Intermission: Retirement, Reconnection, Renewal
(Jeff is here)

Act Three: Jeff plays. Jeffrey's interests include psychology, spirituality, finance, writing, cooking, golfing, joy, fun, friendship, and family. He and Marilyn have three children, four grandchildren.

earthly spirituality

Jeff Imber

i'm no longer out to change the world
only to change the world in me
if in the process of living
from this inner pattern
i inspire touch and
heal others
so be it
if not
so be it
in either case
it's for me to live out
the meaning of my being
keeping my feet on the path
and breathing in spirit as I walk

Rena Davis

Rena Davis is a retired Army Sergeant residing in Sterling Heights, Michigan. She is married to Jason Davis, and they have five kids. Though she is busy taking care of her family, writing is her passion.

This is her fourth contribution to *Sterling Script: A Local Author Collection.* Her first submission, "Army Strong," was her debut into the writing world. This year's piece, "Love on the Battlefield," is a romance based on her time in the army.

She has continued her love of the literary word by creating BookHavenMagazine.com, dedicated to book reviews and articles on writing. Conteur Publishing, her small indie press, is dedicated to publishing creative works as well as writing aids in digital and print format on Etsy.

Her current projects include the Legion and St. Andrews Prep novella series. Book one in each of these will be available in the near future.

Love on the Battlefield

Rena Davis

The desert heat pounded on the soldiers as they gathered in the motor pool for their mission brief. Sweat dripped down their backs as they stood in full battle gear, the desert sand sticking everywhere.

"Today's mission should be an easy one," Master Sergeant yelled over the roar of the Humvee's engines. "Alpha Team will set the charges. Bravo Team will create a secure perimeter around the blast site. Charlie Team will secure the main roads into the area. Now, move out."

Dismissed, they headed to their respective vehicles for final prep and inspections.

"Who is that?" asked Specialist Jason Larson. She had milk chocolate skin, a voluptuous body, and a smile. A smile that had him frozen in place.

"Who?" Specialist Andrew Seamon followed Jason's line of sight. "Her?" His battle buddy was speaking to him, but it sounded as if he was miles away. Jason nodded.

"That's the Commo Rep. She's loading and checking the radios."

Jason watched her maneuver from truck to truck.

"INCOMING!!" a soldier screamed from the fence line.

AK-47 rounds rained in, hitting the earth. Soldiers scattered, kicking up dirt as they ran for cover. Jason followed behind the Commo Rep.

"Go to the bunker. I'll call it in." She made a beeline for the office and grabbed the handset from the radio. "TOC Main, this is Motor Pool, over." Her breath jagged.

"Motor Pool, this is TOC Main, over."

"Incoming rounds from the south end of the Motor Pool, over."

"Roger that, Motor Pool, sending out Q.R.F."

"Roger, out." She dropped the handset and ran into the bunker as the base alarm sounded.

Leaning against the side wall across from her, Jason turned to face her. Chin down, he tilted his head to see her. He couldn't stop focusing on her. His angel. His light in this desert storm.

She caught his eye and smiled.

His heart stopped. He played out his pickup lines in his head. "Hey," or "Wanna get dinner?" or even "Jesus turned water into wine. I'm just trying to turn you into mine." He didn't like any of them.

He steeled himself, took a deep breath, and stepped forward when "ALL CLEAR! ALL CLEAR!" bellowed through the loudspeakers.

Soldiers poured out of the bunkers and headed to their supervisors for accountability.

#

Seamon and Jason grabbed their gear from the truck and headed towards the ordinance cache. "Why didn't you say anything to her?"

"I did." Jason breathed heavily, weighed down by his gear. "At least I did in my head. I couldn't think of the right thing to say."

"Dude! You never had a problem talking to women before."

"Man, I don't know. I got all sweaty, and the words, they wouldn't come out."

"Dude, you got it bad." Seamon laughed. They arrived at a gaping hole in the ground and stared into it.

"Whatever, get to work."

Seamon set the explosive charges around the perimeter of the hole while Jason followed behind him, double-checking his work. Once set, they hopped into their vehicle and headed out of the kill zone.

"Alpha Team set."

"Bravo Team set."

"Charlie Team set."

"All teams set. Fire in the hole."

BOOM! The earth shook around them as white phosphorus smoke filled the air, spreading closer and closer to the established perimeter.

"Alpha Team, move back. Move back now!" Master Sergeant radioed in.

They maneuvered their vehicle back. The cloud enveloped the inside of the perimeter and swirled toward them.

"Dude," Seamon said, "are we sure we moved back far enough? I don't want it to melt the Humvee with us in it."

The smoke continued to grow. Butts clenched, they pushed back in their seats. Seamon prayed. Jason was never religious, but even he threw up a prayer. The smoke hovered at the perimeter line. They released the breath they didn't realize they were holding.

"That was close," Seamon said.

"No shit, dude." Jason wiped the sweat from his forehead. "Any closer, and we would've been done for."

"Good thing Sarge told us to move back."

The air cleared. They packed up and headed back to base.

#

Master Sergeant walked up with a box in his hands. "Specialist Larson, I need you to take these handhelds to the Commo shop for repair."

"Roger that, Master Sergeant."

Jason unstrapped his body armor. His sweaty combat shirt stuck to his chest. He switched his kevlar helmet for his soft cap, grabbed the box, and headed to the Commo shop near the motor pool office.

Inside, his angel stood at the counter.

"How can I help you?" she said, smiling.

He stared at her.

"Is that for me?" She reached out to receive the box in Jason's hands.

"Yes. Master Sergeant Reeves asked me to bring these handhelds down for repair."

"Do you know what's wrong with them?" She took the box from him.

"No."

"That's fine. Follow me." She headed to the workbench in the middle of the office. "Take a seat while I run the diagnostics and write up the work orders."

Jason followed her and sat on a stool near the workbench. The Commo Shop wasn't that big. The metal walls of the shipping container made the office seem clinical.

"What's your name?" she asked.

"Specialist Larson. First name Jason."

She scribbled his answer on the work order.

"What Company are you with?"

"Alpha Company, Sergeant. G-3." He took a steadying breath. "How come I've never seen you before?"

"Did you just say, how come?"

"What's wrong with how come?"

"Nothing." With an upward turn of her lips, she chuckled to herself. "Maybe you've never needed my help before. I'm what people call a workaholic."

"Do you like fixing radios, Sergeant?" He rolled his eyes. *Stupid question, Jason.*

"Sometimes. I prefer working on computers, though," she

said. "By the way, it's Sergeant Kofa. But you can call me Victoria when we are alone. I hate the formality inherent in using what my friends and I like to call my military name."

"Ok, Victoria." He smiled. "I dabble in computers myself, a little."

"That's cool." She jotted down the serial numbers from the back of the radios on the work order form.

While Victoria processed the order, they exchanged childhood stories and backgrounds. Jason grew up in the Midwest near Detroit, Michigan, and Victoria had a mischievous history skipping class at boarding school near Washington DC.

As their laughter subsided, Jason fiddled with the soldering gun on the bench. "Is this your first deployment?"

"No. It's my fourth. This is your first, isn't it?"

"Yeah, can you tell?"

"No, not at all." She smirked. "Here you go. I'll send you an email when the radios are ready for pickup."

#

Jason and Seamon walked into the food court area near the PX. As they headed to the Pizza Hut stand, Jason noticed his angel was standing in line. "Hey, there." He tapped Victoria on the shoulder.

She jumped and turned around. Her hand reached for her 9mm pistol on her right hip. "Oh," she covered her heart with her hand and breathed a sigh of relief. "Hey. Specialist Larson, right?"

"Good memory." They moved up in line.

"By the way, your radios should be available for pickup tomorrow. Hopefully."

"That's quick," said Jason. "Thanks for taking good care of me."

"I had to push it to the top of the priority list because of your lieutenant. They are 'imperative for an upcoming mission,'" she said. "His words."

"Sergeant Kofa. Order for Sergeant Kofa." The Iraqi National shouted from the pickup window.

"That's me." She grabbed her food. "See you around."

Victoria joined her friends, plopped the pizza and paper plates on the table, and took a seat next to Specialist Maria Flores.

"Who was that?" Flores asked.

"Who was what?"

"Now she is trying to play dumb." Sergeant Kimberly Smith grabbed a plate and a slice of pizza.

"What are you guys talking about?" Victoria said.

"Who was the stud you were talking to at the food stand?" Flores asked again.

"Him? He's the G-3's Commo rep."

"And?" Smith asked.

"And what?" Victoria took a bite of her pepperoni, bacon, and sausage pizza.

"There was an awful lot of chitchat in line," surmised Flores.

"And smiling," Smith added.

"He was just saying hi, and I told him I'd have his radios ready tomorrow."

"Riiiight," Flores and Smith said in unison. Both with smirks on their faces.

"As an objective observer..." Smith cleared her throat. "It looked like he was more interested in you than in his radios."

"You think?" Victoria smiled.

"Gotcha! I knew you liked him." Flores smacked the table in triumph.

"Come on. You and I both know that deployment romances never last." Victoria finished her slice and took another.

"Who knows? You guys could be the exception." Smith sipped her Coke.

"Plus, even if it doesn't last, he is way too cute to pass up. That's coming from me, and I don't even like men." Flores inhaled her last bite. "You know who he looks like to me? Jensen Ackles."

"Who?" Smith asked.

"I can't believe you just said that. Dean Winchester." Victoria waited for recognition. "From *Supernatural*. The best TV show ever." Victoria rolled her eyes.

"Oh, yeah. He does," Smith said.

The girls spent the rest of the night laughing and giggling about Jason and Victoria.

#

At the Humvees, Jason approached Victoria.

"Hey," Jason said.

"Oh, hey, what's up? Do you need something?"

"No," he said.

"Ok?"

Jason looked down at his feet. "Would you go to dinner with me?"

Victoria's wrench slipped causing the Humvee's battery to spark. "Dinner?"

"Yeah, dinner."

Her stomach flipped. "Sure. When?"

He perked up. "Tonight?"

With a smile, she said, "I'd love to."

He grinned. "Great. I'll meet you at the food court around 1900 hours."

"See you there." She picked up her tool box and sauntered to the next vehicle.

#

Jason pulled up to the food court in a black Suburban. His angel stood outside the entrance. He smiled to himself and jumped out of the car to meet her. She was wearing the

101

summer physical training uniform. Black shorts with the word Army in silver reflective writing on the left leg and a grey shirt with Army written across the chest. A yellow reflective belt around her waistline held her pistol.

"You look great," he said when he reached her.

"Thanks. It's PT chic." They laughed and walked back to the Suburban. He opened the door for her.

"I thought we were having dinner here?" she said as she slid into the passenger seat. "Tell me we are not going to the DFAC."

"We're not going to the DFAC." He chuckled, closed the door behind her, and hustled to the driver's seat.

"Then where are we going?"

"I figured we would go over to the Liberty side food court and get some pizza. Away from prying eyes."

"That sounds good." She buckled up.

They drove ten minutes from Camp Victory across the bridge to Camp Liberty.

At the food court, they decided on Pizza Hut.

"What's your favorite type of pizza?" Victoria asked.

"Detroit style, hands down." Jason served her a slice of pizza before getting his own.

"What is Detroit style?"

"It's pretty much a deep-dish pizza with the sauce on top in two straight lines down the length of the pizza." He took a bite of his pepperoni pizza. "What's yours?"

"I'd have to say stuffed crust," she said between bites. "It's the best of both worlds. Gooey cheese in a pizza crust. Heaven."

They laughed. "What's your MOS?" Victoria asked.

"13 Delta."

"What's that?"

"We send ordinance rounds to a location based on coordinates from the soldiers on the ground," he explained, "but I spend most of my time this deployment doing EOD missions or being our section's commo person."

"I guess that means we will work together a lot this deployment."

"I guess it's fate."

She loved how he made her laugh, and he loved how easy it was to talk to her. Done eating, they headed back to his SUV. They looked up at the night sky filled with light, not from stars but from the floodlights all over the base.

"What are you thinking about?" he asked.

"Do you really want to know?"

"Yes."

"I was wondering why you haven't kissed me yet."

Jason looked shocked. His stomach filled with butterflies. He leaned over the seat and cradled the side of her face with his right hand. Caressing her cheek with his thumb, he guided her face closer to his. When their lips met, her whole body weakened. When their lips parted, her body cried out as if to say, "No, don't stop."

"How was that?" he asked.

"I guess it was ok."

"Just ok?" He pouted.

"Maybe I need another to be sure."

He leaned in again, but the sudden blare of the base alarms stopped him short. "Oh, shit, time to go."

Jason raced back to Camp Victory. The wheels of the SUV kicked up dust, leaving a wake of sand behind the vehicle. They had to make it back as soon as possible. No one knew they were on Camp Liberty. As they passed Saddam's palace, Victoria spotted a bright dot in the sky.

"Is that—?" She pointed to the sky.

"A tracer round, from the C-RAM." Jason floored the gas pedal.

"Why does it look like it's coming at us?"

"Because it is."

Victoria strained to see out of the windshield. "Three

deployments and I've never had a rocket coming at me."

"Focus your eyes. Look for the vapor trail behind it."

Victoria's heart dropped. The round was heading straight for them, bright green in the sky, hurtling towards the front of their vehicle.

Through clenched teeth, Victoria said, "Jason, drive faster!"

"I'm driving as fast as I can!"

"I don't think we're going to make it. It's going to hit us."

The C-RAM round impacted the rocket. The explosion sent waves of pressure through the area, nearly flipping the SUV. Jason swerved, then regained control. The tires screeched. They pulled up and bolted for the nearest bunker. Safe, for now.

#

Jason walked into the motor pool with a smile on his face. Despite the interruption of their first date, the last three days were amazing. He scanned the lot on the way to his Humvee. There she was, his angel.

He sidled up behind her. "Good morning," he whispered into her ear.

She jumped. "Hey." She reached for him but thought better of it. Her eyes scanned the area. Keep it professional, girl. "Are you on today's mission?"

"Yeah." He knelt down in front of her as she sat in the driver's seat with the door open. "Tonight, my friends and I are having a little BBQ in our CHU area." He held her hand. "Will you come?"

"Is this a meet-the-friends date?" she asked.

"You could call it that."

"Then I'd love to."

He squeezed her hand. "I'll see you tonight."

Jason shot Victoria a smile and a wave as he left the motor pool for his mission. The convoy drove through the city, roads littered with trash. Insurgents used the trash to hide their improvised explosive devices, which made the city areas stressful.

When they reached the countryside, Jason relaxed a little. His mind wandered back to his angel.

"You're thinking about her, aren't you?" Seamon teased.

"Why would you ask that?" Jason shifted in the passenger seat.

"Because your cheeks are red. Plus, you're smiling to yourself." Laughed Seamon.

"You're cooking the burgers tonight, right?"

"Sure."

"I'll get the drinks from the PX when we get back."

"Dude, you got to calm down. It's going to be fine."

"I just want everything to go well." Jason punched his battle buddy's shoulder.

Their laughter was cut short as Jason grabbed the handset to the radio.

"Stop the vehicle." Jason said. "Troop Leader, this is Alpha Team, over."

"Go ahead, Alpha Team, over."

"There's something in the road up ahead, over."

"Roger that, Alpha Team, break, convoy, this is Troop Leader, stop in place, break, prepare for recovery, over. Buffalo, this is Troop Leader, over."

"Troop Leader, this is Buffalo, over."

"Buffalo, this is Troop Leader, break, move up for inspection, break, unknown object in the road, break, proceed with caution, over."

They moved in a herringbone pattern off to the side of the road. The large, explosive-resistant Buffalo moved up the middle and stopped 100 yards from the object.

"Convoy, this is Troop Leader, break, secure the scene, break, stay vigilant."

They launched the IED robot from the back of the

Buffalo. The robot began its inspection. There were no visual signs of lines or cables. The engineer engaged the controls of the Buffalo's arm. He worked the joysticks to lower and position the scoop at the end of the arm. Slowly, he raised the object. A loud boom sent shock waves throughout the area.

"Buffalo, is everyone alright?"

"Roger that. The arm is destroyed, over."

"Alpha Team, this is Troop Leader, break, can you see the Buffalo, over."

Jason radioed back. "Roger, over."

The ground erupted on the right side of the road, triggering a chain of explosions. Smoke filled the air as shrapnel flew.

"Pull back, pull back! What was that? Over." Master Sergeant yelled through the radio.

"TOC Main, this is Alpha Troop Leader, over."

"Alpha Troop Leader, this is TOC Main, over."

"We're hit, break, request recovery and extraction, over!"

#

Victoria listened, while Jason's convoy radioed into the Tactical Operations Center. Her heart pounded. Louder and louder it echoed in her ear, increasing as TOC Main continued to get reports in from the Alpha Troop leader.

"Sergeant Kofa," the Battalion Sergeant Major called.

"Yes, Sergeant Major."

"I'm sure you heard what they radioed in."

"Yes, Sergeant Major."

"Get your tools and head down to the motor pool. Rendezvous with the recovery team."

"Roger that, Sergeant Major."

She grabbed her bag and raced out the door. At a normal pace, it's about a fifteen minute walk, but Victoria made it there in eight. Soldiers were already erecting a big canopy to house the destroyed vehicles being towed in. Victoria jumped in to help. She needed to stay busy.

"Sergeant Kofa," Chief Sharp approached her.

"Yes, Chief."

"When the vehicles get here, pull all the communications equipment out of them."

"Roger that."

"If you need help, let me know."

"I should be good, Chief." He walked away when she called out, "Hey, Chief."

"Yes, Sergeant."

"Do we have a list of the injured yet?"

"There were soldiers rushed to the ER, but I don't have any names."

"Thanks, Chief." Victoria said, her voice breaking.

Chief Sharp walked back and placed a supportive hand on her shoulder. "Focus on the tasks you're assigned and pray that those injured pull through. That's all we can do right now."

She felt the tears waiting to explode. Victoria closed her eyes and exhaled. "You're right. Thanks, Chief."

Victoria watched as the vehicles arrived, one was a flat piece of metal in flames. She braced herself and got to work. The vehicles smelled of copper and the remnants of a bonfire. The sight of blood and flesh on one of the radio mounts as she pulled it out made her choke back her tears.

"Hey, chica." Flores walked up and placed a comforting hand on her shoulder.

Victoria turned around. "What are you doing here?"

"I heard what happened and rushed down here as soon as I could."

"Why? What do you know?"

"Jason. He was one of the injured."

Victoria felt the ground slip from underneath her. Her head spun. "Are you sure?"

"Yes." Flores caught her as she collapsed. She closed

Victoria's toolbox. "Here, sit."

Breathing in and out, Victoria tried to regain control. Flores drove her friend to the hospital on Camp Liberty.

They walked into the emergency waiting room. Seamon paced the hallway. "Specialist Seamon," Victoria called out.

"Sergeant Kofa." He touched her shoulder. "He's ok. It could've been a lot worse."

"What happened? Where was he hit?"

"I pulled off to the right side of the road. The ground erupted under us on the passenger side." He guided her to a seat before anyone noticed her wobbly stance. "There's shrapnel in his legs. They have him in surgery right now."

She dropped her head in her hands. "I want to be here for him, but I have to get back for a stupid briefing."

"There is nothing you can do for him right now." He grabbed her hands in his. "I promise, I will let you know when he's allowed visitors. Trust me, he'll know you were here for him."

"Come on," said Flores.

Victoria got back to the TOC just in time for the end-of-shift briefing. She could only think of Jason. She fought the tears welling in her eyes as they reviewed the events of the day.

On cue, she stood and faced the Battalion Sergeant Major. "I removed the electronics from the destroyed vehicles; they're in the Commo shop. Next slide, please. These are the serial numbers of the equipment we recovered. Some had their serial numbers burned away, so I had to go off of my spreadsheet from my pre-mission checks. I will have them sent to G-6 by the end of day tomorrow." She sat back down.

"Medics," Sergeant Major said.

"There were four soldiers injured in today's hit. As you can see, they are all currently labeled stable by the hospital."

"Have their families been contacted?" Sergeant Major jotted notes into his field notebook.

"Yes, Sergeant Major. Next slide, please. These are the next of kin that were contacted and when."

Victoria stared at the screen. Next to Jason's name was "Stacy Larson, wife." She felt the room spin. *That son of a bitch*, she thought.

#

Seamon walked into Jason's hospital room. "Hey, big guy."

Jason lifted his head, but let it fall back. "What happened out there?"

"You were hit with shrapnel. Surgery was a success. And before you ask, yes, Sergeant Kofa is here. I've been keeping her updated."

He relaxed. "When can I get out of here?"

"Probably not for a bit. You're on a lot of drugs, man. I'm gonna go find out." Seamon headed for the door, where Victoria stood. He placed a hand on her shoulder and gave her a smile before continuing out of the room.

"Hey," Victoria said.

"Hey," Jason sat up in his bed. "I'm glad you're here."

She sat next to his bed. "I'm glad you're ok."

"Yeah, me too." He studied her face. "Is everything ok?" He smiled and scanned his body with his hands. "As you can see, I am fine."

"Maybe, but we aren't."

"What does that mean?"

"How's your wife? Have you called her yet? I'm sure she's worried."

Jason's heart sank into his stomach. He stared at her, holding back the urge to vomit. "It's not what you think."

She popped up from the chair. "Then what is it like?"

"We are legally separated."

"Right." She crossed her arms.

"We plan to get divorced after the deployment."

"Why didn't you tell me in the beginning?"

"I really like you. I wanted you to give me a chance."

"All you had to do was be honest with me, Jason." Victoria turned to leave.

"Wait. I'm sorry. Please believe me." He reached toward her and knocked over the cup of water on his bedside table. A loud clunk sounded in the room as the cup hit the floor. "I didn't lie when I told you how I feel about you. And I'm not lying when I say my marriage has been over long before I had ever met you."

She turned back, picked up the cup, and mopped up the water with tissue from the table. "I have to go."

#

There was a rattle at Victoria's door. "Come in."

Jason walked into the Commo shop.

She rolled her eyes when he came in. "Can I help you?"

"G-3 needs these computers reconfigured." He placed a box on the entrance table.

She pulled the box of the laptops towards her and pulled out some work order forms. They stood in silence at the service desk as she filled out the paperwork.

"It's been a couple of days since I've seen you. How have you been?"

"Good." She stared at the forms. "You?"

He fiddled with the pens on the counter. "Missing you."

"If I'm being honest," she flipped over one form and started on the next. "I miss you, too."

He cleared his throat. "We're having another barbecue at our CHU tonight. You're welcome to come. No pressure."

She looked up from the forms. A familiar longing shone through his gaze. "I'll think about it."

Her friends talked her into going to the barbecue. Flores told her to look at it like a fact-finding mission. Smith reassured her they would stay with her as backup.

Jason introduced the girls to his friends. They shared

stories around the picnic table about deployments, both recent and past. They talked about things they've seen or heard. The rotting smell of garbage in the streets, the excessive attacks on the base, and more. Relief filled the air. Jason's platoon celebrated being alive after the last Buffalo mission.

Victoria got along with his friends. His buddies kept throwing out comments like "Are you sure you want to settle for him" or "You're totally awesome."

Flores and Smith gave their stamps of approval, solidifying his place in Victoria's heart. Reservations aside, she was in love with this man.

#

The next morning, Victoria visited her friend Bailey in S-1, the administration department.

"I heard about Jason, girl. How's he doing?"

"He's doing as well as can be expected. He's the reason I came to see you today."

With a raised eyebrow, she said, "What's up?"

"Can you check into his marital status for me?"

"Now, you know I'm not supposed to, but for you, of course. Take a seat." Sergeant Bailey typed as Victoria made herself comfortable in a chair next to her desk. "Why am I looking up his marital status?"

"Because according to a briefing I was at, he's married, but he said they're separated."

"I see. That makes sense." She typed away. "Looks like that's true. File says married, but legally separated."

"Really." Victoria exhaled. "Thanks, Bailey."

"No problem. We got to look out for each other, girl."

"Ain't that the truth." They laughed. "I'll talk to you later."

#

A thunderous roar echoed through the base. The earth

rocked. A loud, wailing sound broadcast through the base speakers. Soldiers raced to find the nearest bunker, some falling to their knees.

Two consecutive rounds soared in, striking damaging blows to the roof of Saddam's Palace. Bunkers all over base crumbled under the weight of the incoming rockets.

Jason and Seamon raced out of the DFAC. They ran to the nearest bunker just as a round hit the side entrance they'd exited. Huddled in the bunker, Jason stared in disbelief as another round hit caving in one side of the bunker next to them. He moved towards the crumbling bunker.

Seamon grabbed his arm.

"We have to help them," Jason said as he pulled from his grasp.

"Fine," Seamon screamed. "Let's go."

They guided troops to their bunker. Seamon and Jason worked to free a soldier trapped under the rubble. They removed the debris and carried the last soldier to safety.

"Push in," Jason screamed as they stumbled in, injured soldier in tow.

Everyone stood shoulder to shoulder, hunched under the low ceiling of the bunker. The smell of copper and dirt filled the dusty air.

"Take off your belt." Jason placed the soldier on the ground and grabbed the belt from Seamon. He wrapped it around the injured soldier's leg to create a tourniquet.

The base speakers bellowed, "ALL CLEAR, ALL CLEAR."

Soldiers scampered from their hiding place and headed to their platoon's rally point. Jason stayed with the injured while Seamon retrieved the medics. Jason stood observing the aftermath of the attack.

He only had one thought in his mind: where is Victoria?

When the medics arrived to tend to the injured, Jason hurried for his squad's rally point for accountability.

"Larson," Seamon yelled across the CHU lot. "Have you checked in with Sergeant First Class Malone yet?"

"Yeah. Have you heard what got hit?"

"The palace and a couple of CHU areas." Seamon sat on the picnic bench in front of their CHU. "Before you ask, no, I don't know if Victoria's got hit."

"I need the keys." Jason reached his hand out to Seamon. "Now!"

Jason jumped into the black Suburban and raced to search for Victoria. When he pulled up, he saw several soldiers outside. He searched the faces of everyone he passed as he walked to her CHU. No Victoria.

He walked up to the nearest NCO he could find wearing an 18th Airborne Corps patch. "Excuse me, Sergeant. Have you seen Sergeant Kofa?"

"No, I'm sorry."

Jason went to her quarters. Only the base of the structure remained. He wasn't one for prayer, but at that moment, he dropped to his knees and pleaded with the man upstairs. "Please, God. Please. Let her be ok."

"Excuse me," he said to a passing soldier. "Do you know what happened to the soldiers that live in these CHU's?"

"The medics took them to the hospital morgue."

"Are you sure?"

"Yeah."

Jason's vision blurred. His mouth went dry. It hurt to breathe. He could feel his airway closing. Tears welled in his eyes, but he wouldn't let them drop. He picked himself up, bolted for his SUV, and raced back to get Seamon. He needed his best friend with him to check the hospital.

"Seamon," he yelled as he darted for the common area. He stopped in his tracks when he saw Seamon with another figure.

"Jason?" Victoria walked toward him.

Jason froze, eyes wide, face pale. "Are you really here?"

113

"Yeah. Why wouldn't I be."

He threw his arms around her. The tears he was holding back fell from his eyes. "I thought I had lost you."

"Why?" She tried to pull back, and he hugged tighter.

"Your CHU was hit."

"What? Seriously?!"

"Listen, I know you're upset with me." Jason pulled her back to look at her. "But after seeing your CHU and thinking I had lost you…" he choked up. "There is no way I can live without you. I love you, Victoria Kofa."

Tears filled her eyes. She cradled his face in her hands. "I love you, too."

Rebecca Eve Schweitzer

Rebecca Eve Schweitzer is a writer, artist, editor, social media consultant, marketer, zine maker, and word nerd based in Metro-Detroit. She has an overactive imagination, hordes books like a dragon, and would like to be a unicorn or phoenix should she ever be forced to grow up.

She is a member of the Sterling Script editorial board, a founding member of the Tuesday Morning Writers, and an active participant of the Sterling Heights Creative Writing Workshop. Her writing, art, zines, and blog can be found at www.beccaeve.com.

Feathers
In response to Emily Dickinson

Rebecca Eve Schweitzer

i am the thing with feathers
baring my own soul
i will not sing some sweet song
but rather scream my all

i will not flutter with the wind
no matter how sore the storm
nothing will abash this bird
my flight serves to warn

through the chillest land
and over strangest sea
regardless of extremity
i — never cease to be

To-do List

Rebecca Eve Schweitzer

Today, we test mirror affirmations
Tell our inverted self we are
The baddest bitch on the block
No, the whole neighborhood

We have confidence and kind eyes
We have long legs and thick thighs
In a good way

We look past the dust on the glass
The piles of laundry around the room
They don't define us

This week we start a file
For compliments and awards
We age out of report cards
Craft our own gold stars

We take that honorable mention
With a little extra pride

This month, we track
Not productivity but inspiration
We mark down the ideas
Spend them before they expire

We're piling up projects
With no deadlines

This year, we forget to
Make a vision board
We walk, without resolution
No longer trying to plot the course

You shouldn't write a poem for the boy who won't text you back

Rebecca Eve Schweitzer

But you will

You will craft a poem about the words
in his head writing over themselves to
avoid spilling out of his mouth or
fingers, clenched closed untouching

You will create in that poem an elaborate
fantasy in which you stand in front of him
at a poetry reading speaking those words
you wrote about a boy

Who won't text you back

But who will in your fantasy
come to your poetry reading
because in poetry things work out
or they don't

Because in poetry you are
your own response but real
life things float like the texts
sent maybe to a boy

Maybe to a void

Which is why you should write
a poem for the boy who won't
text you back as a response to
yourself a poet full of words

Mary Rose Kreger

From Army public affairs to convent life to marriage and motherhood, Mary Rose Kreger's journey has been filled with twists and turns. Wherever she's journeyed, she's always been writing stories. She lives in the metro Detroit area with her family, where she writes fantasy tales for teens and blogs about her spiritual journey on www.monasteryinmyheart.com. Mary also shares faith-based poems and fantasy quotes on her Instagram account, @faithandfantasy1.

Her short fiction piece, "The Broken Thread," is an excerpt from the YA fantasy novel, *The Indigo Dozen*.

The Broken Thread

Mary Rose Kreger

Around three o-clock on a Wednesday afternoon, a mysterious letter arrived at the Lee apartment door. It was delivered by a messenger boy who fled the scene as soon as he'd dropped the letter into Dylan's hands.

"There's a letter for you, Father," Dylan said, as he carried the note from the entranceway to the family dining room. He risked a quick glance at the letter's seal: a swirl of black and gold wax, imprinted with a sharp-clawed bird of prey.

Isn't that Lord Amaranth's symbol?

Lord Amaranth was the second most powerful person in Valeria, second only to Queen Colette herself. He had been away from Valeria for months, waging war in the neighboring country of Avalon.

Has Amaranth returned to Valeria then? What does he want with my father?

Dylan had entered the dining room now where his father could see him, so he feigned indifference and handed the letter over a plate of butter pastries.

When Sir Hamish Lee saw the letter's seal, his face blanched white as paper. His eyes narrowed as he opened the letter and read its contents.

"What is it, darling?" asked Dylan's mother, Tiaras.

Hamish folded the letter shut and slipped it inside his jacket.

"I'm going out tonight for supper, dearest. I've a business meeting in the Western Quays."

"The Quays?" Tiaras repeated with distaste. "That's an odd corner of the city."

Hamish didn't answer. He was too busy grinding his half-eaten pastry into a pile of powdery crumbles.

"I'll return by the tenth bell. If I don't, send Charles to fetch me. I'll leave an address." Hamish swigged the last of his afternoon tea and whiskey, then rose from the table.

His wife frowned. "Be careful, darling. We have many enemies here."

"Aye, my love. Stay in the apartments while I'm away." It was a hopeful request, rather than a command. Here in Valeria, it was Tiaras, not Hamish, who typically made the family plans. Tiaras was a countess, while Hamish's status and reputation were not so sterling.

His title here was Hamish the Traitor. Ten years ago, he'd betrayed Bran, the King of Avalon, into Amaranth's hands. His treachery had been against the Avalian king, not Queen Colette, but it didn't matter. No one in Valeria trusted Hamish.

Dylan didn't trust him, either. Which was why he planned to follow his father to the Western Quays tonight.

There were questions Dylan needed answered, and tonight maybe he would get them: where did Hamish really stand? Had he truly traveled all the way from Scotland to Valeria to make his atonement?

Or was he still Amaranth's man?

#

Later that evening, Dylan followed his father into a bustling, shiny tearoom called *The Sapphire Sword*. It stood on the western waterfront of Maia Mellon, just a stone's throw from the shipyards lining the Sparkling Sea.

The tearoom's patrons were dressed in the latest and finest Valerian fashions, and nearly all of them had a rapier or glass blade strapped to their hips. They lounged in elegant, lacquered chairs, sipping cocktails and gossiping around gleaming hardwood tables. A troupe of musicians, dressed in luxurious reds and tangerine, strummed delicate tunes on stringed lyres.

The vast space was littered with ferns and ornamental trees, providing both privacy and ambience at each table. It also caused Dylan to lose his father more than once between the fluttering emerald fronds.

However, it was difficult to lose a man of Hamish's stature for long. Dylan spotted his father's long coattails whipping around a cluster of shrubs, before once again vanishing into the greenery.

He marked Hamish's location—a secluded table on the tearoom's left-hand side—and found an empty booth only a few yards away. He dropped into the booth and cast a cloak on the adjoining seat, as if reserving a space for a guest. A golden maple shrub hid Dylan from view, but he could just make out his father's face through the branches.

"Greetings, my lord," Hamish said, his voice neutral and respectful. "I admit, I didn't expect to have the honor of meeting you in person."

Dylan leaned back in his chair with surprise. *Aye, now I can see his pale, ugly face. Lord Amaranth himself is here.*

"This is a meeting we must have in person, Lee," Amaranth purred. "Who else could I confide in about my...difficulty?"

Difficulty? What, does he have warts in an unseemly place or something?

A server stepped up, took their orders for drinks, and left the table.

Hamish didn't answer Amaranth's question. In fact, his father looked almost bored, although Amaranth could surely kill him in an instant, should Hamish say anything to offend him.

But Father's too smart to say anything of the sort.

The server returned with their drinks. They'd both ordered *Salamanca*, a strong, fermented fruit drink laced with spices.

"Fiona won't speak to me."

Hamish tapped the side of his drinking glass. The reddish liquid quivered at his touch.

"I see. And when did this begin?"

"After the retreat from Cair Tintagel," Amaranth supplied. "Since then, she will have nothing at all to do with me."

"What, you mean after the night you brutally tortured and murdered her son?" Hamish sipped his drink, made a face at its flavor. "I can't imagine why."

Dylan grew still, felt a chill come over him despite the warm stuffiness of the tearoom.

Has something happened to Will Owain?

Amaranth shifted in his seat, then took a long draught of the *Salamanca*.

"I was keeping my promise. I told Fiona that if the boy came for her, I would break him. And she would watch." He leaned forward, so that Dylan could just make out his macabre expression between the green fronds. "Except...Owain wouldn't break. He chose death first to save his princess."

The villain scowled as if Hamish had accused him.

"Yes, he got the death he wanted. And now my Fiona's remembered just how much she hates me."

A burst of laughter at a nearby table clashed dissonantly with Amaranth's unhappy news.

Owain. Is he really dead?

Hamish shook his head. "Ten years ago, you bound Fiona to yourself with two threads: her husband, and their son. Now that you've cut one of those thread..." His voice trailed off ominously.

Amaranth slipped something out of his pocket. Dylan couldn't see what it was from his position, except that it was small enough to fit in the palm of the villain's hand.

"Show me how to win her back, Lee. I need her."

His father leaned back in his chair. "There's no need to threaten me, my lord. I am fully aware of how easily you can destroy me and my family." A faint smile crossed his lips. "But, as it were, I am inclined to help you with your...difficulty. The solution is simple."

Amaranth's eyes glinted like steel in the lamplight. "Go on."

"You killed Owain, yet he's still giving you grief. So bring him back from the dead."

What?

"I have heard a rumor here in Valeria, my lord," his father continued, "and if I have heard it, surely you, Master of all Rumors, have heard it also. They say that—"

"Anything else for you tonight, sir?"

Dylan startled, looked up into the polite, bland face of his server.

"Excuse me? Oh. Two lavender honey cakes, if you please. And also my script."

The server left, but Dylan had missed the juicy piece of gossip. The next thing he heard was Amaranth slamming his glass on the table.

"That's impossible! There was enough of his blood to bathe in by the end."

"If he's dead, he's dead," Hamish said. "But if the rumor is true...what is to prevent you from finding Owain and bringing him back to Fiona? You could tell her: I killed your son once, yes, but I regret what I have done. Here, see—I have returned him to you."

This answer seemed to please Amaranth.

"I take life away, and give it back again." His pallid face took on a feverish glow. "Nothing is beyond me."

'Ranth is both mad, and full of it, Dylan thought with a shudder.

127

"Yes, my lord. Rewrite the tragic story, and make yourself the hero. The merciful savior."

The villain nodded with increasing enthusiasm. "Excellent. And how shall I acquire him?"

"Put a bounty on his head. Something to attract the notice of every man-hunter in Valeria and Avalon alike."

"And this proposition gives you no qualms?" The question hung in the air for a long, quivering moment, before Hamish squashed the villain's doubts.

"You asked for advice, my lord, and I have given it. I can personally lead the assignment, if you wish." He ran his fingers along the table's lacquered edge. "In return, I hope you will remember me and my family in a favorable light."

"Bring Owain to me, Lee, and your family will be protected," Amaranth answered. "But if your plan fails, I cannot guarantee their safety."

Hamish's massive hand swallowed Amaranth's as they shook on the deal.

Father has to follow through with his plan now. Or our family is finished.

The server returned with the honey cakes, which was lucky, since this hid Dylan from his father's view. By the time the server left the table, both Amaranth and Hamish were gone.

Dylan stayed a while longer, nibbling one of the ultra-sweet cakes and reflecting on what he'd overheard.

There's got to be a way to save Owain without jeopardizing my family's safety, he decided. *And I know just the men to help me with the task.*

He left a few coins on the table with his script, then exited the tearoom by another route. He wasn't heading home quite yet.

It was time to ask a favor from his friends in the Indigo Dozen.

Saint Agnes Day, January 21, 2019

Mary Rose Kreger

Saint Agnes, virgin martyr,
Tonight a Blood Moon rises in your honor,
Sweeping through Cancer's pyramid of stars.

Eclipsed by the Earth and hidden in its shadow
People seek and cannot find you, you rare thing—
They fail to see because you are not what they expect:
Neither bright, nor red, nor breathless in your beauty.

Rather, you are obscured,
Lost in smoke and shadows even at your fullness
You seem spent, even in the midst of your bloody passion
Charms all but hidden from the eyes of mortals.

Yet eternity paints a different picture of you
In that place where good and secret things come to light,
The invisible ones made visible at last.

And so, too, I hope to not always be hidden and forgotten,
My blue flame eclipsed in unspoken words, unwritten
    expressions
Consuming my heart from the inside out.

Mary Merlo

Mary Merlo is a retired Human Resource Manager in the automotive industry. She writes poetry, memoir, short stories, and children's picture books. Her work has appeared in a number of literary publications, as well as online magazines, and she's received awards from DWW for children's stories. She is a member of Detroit Working Writers (DWW), Poetry Society of Michigan (PSM) and Society of Children's Book Writers and Illustrators (SCBWI). She enjoys time with family, especially grandchildren, a source of inspiration for storytelling. She believes that skills developed writing poetry provide an excellent basis for expanding creative interests into other literary genres.

Second Chance Garden

Mary Merlo

In a little garden beneath
the Shadblow tree
I plant gifted flowers
when they no longer thrive.
I don't discard Easter lilies
when trumpet flowers
droop, green leaves
still alive, I return them
to the earth, hope they may
survive. First appearing,
yellow daffodils
revived to my surprise,
tiny teacups on star-shaped
saucers announce the start
of Spring. Last year's
purple hyacinths bloom
like bundled starfish at play.
Mother's Day tulips, no two
the same, sprout straight
and tall, buds spread pink
petals to greet the world one day.
Fragrant, fussy, coral azaleas,
given by a friend, failed
to triumph over winter snow.
Silent messengers,
foil-wrapped gifts of love,
whisper sadness, joy, romance,
and hope. Even faded flowers
are worthy of a second chance.

L. Broas Mann

Broas Mann received Mechanical Engineering degrees from Illinois Institute of Technology and Northwestern University. That was followed by a fifty-year career at Chrysler Corporation engaged in automotive research, during which time he wrote many technical papers and reports.

Upon retiring, he wanted to continue working with words and ideas, so he turned to writing historical fiction and published four books, three journals of Levi Broas, about the history of his family's pioneering adventures in western Michigan, and *The Journal of Ruth Ann Broas* about the journey from a woman's perspective.

Mann also wrote *On and Off the Road*, an anthology of trips in North America and Europe that he and his wife Marion enjoyed.

The Storm

L. Broas Mann

Major storms are like people. They have distinct personalities. Each is unique in size, shape, intensity, and temperament. A storm can bring blessed relief from heat or drought, or endless joy on snow covered hills and ski trails.

But it can also bluster, ravage, and destroy.
And the worst ones kill.
This is a story about such a storm.

THE BIRTHPLACE
CAPE VERDI ISLANDS
April 14, 1969

Even as a child, Marcos da Costa was fascinated by the weather patterns that drifted over Santa Maria Island off the African coast, 350 miles to the east. He loved watching the shifting cloud formations that filled the sky. His interest continued into Marcos' late teens and was the main reason he went to Portugal and obtained a degree in meteorology at the Institute of Engineering in Coimbra.

Today, as he watched huge thunderheads climb thousands of feet above the churning ocean, he knew, as a spotter for the National Oceanic and Atmospheric Administration, they needed to hear from him. So, using his short wave radio,

133

Marcos alerted his contact at the National Hurricane Center in Miami that a storm was building east of Cape Verdi.

The savannahs of Mauritania and Senegal are spawning grounds for many hurricanes. Today, a large tropical depression moved westward off the African continent and slid toward the Cape Verdi Islands. There, the monstrous forces created by these winds resulted in an irresistible vacuum that sucked up massive amounts of the warm water.

Some of these storms turn north and die out over the cold waters of the Atlantic. But today, Mother Nature decided to push this one all the way to the warm currents of the Gulfstream, the Caribbean, and the Gulf of Mexico.

THE CARRIBEAN
April 17, 1969

Hurricane season in the western Atlantic is defined by the NOAA as June through November, so the storm trackers could not imagine there being such a storm in April. John Adamson, Chief of Staff at the Miami office, was certain his Cape Verde spotter was mistaken.

But Marcos da Costa had never been wrong before, and he was not wrong this time. Soon, Adamson got a message from his spotter in the Lesser Antilles. A Category 3 was making its way through the archipelago—weeks ahead of schedule.

John had not finished preparing the list of storm names for this year, so, in the manner of a police blotter, he gave this one a temporary name: Jane Doe. (Then he made a mental note to thank Marcos for warning him of this pre-season devil.)

Staying south of Puerto Rico, Jane brushed Jamaica and the Caymans, then stepped through the strait between Cancun and the tip of Cuba's westernmost peninsula. She dumped a lot of rain but did only moderate damage.

THE GULF OF MEXICO
April 18, 1969

It had been an unusually warm, sunny winter in the Gulf. The water temperatures, normally in the mid-seventies in April, had risen into the eighties by the time Jane Doe arrived. When she tasted this heady brew, she was ecstatic— you might say "in heat." Her eye was surrounded by a thirsty whirlwind inhaling water by the ton. As she approached the western Gulf, Jane had grown to a Category 5.

Tornados are caused by very transient weather systems, and can appear suddenly, without much warning. A hurricane, on the other hand, does not "sneak up." Most everyone within a few hundred miles knows it's coming. What they don't know is where it's going. And because of that, the NOAA predictions aren't always spot-on, so some people in storm-prone areas don't take them seriously. Oil-riggers tend to fall in this group.

#

DEEPWELL

Deepwell was a huge floating platform known as a Mobile Offshore Drilling Unit. A MODU is not anchored to the sea floor. A computerized navigation system using satellite signals controls powerful thrusters that keep the rig on its target location. Today, Deepwell was positioned above a newly discovered oil and gas field about 100 miles southeast of Corpus Christi.

Pete Hoekmann was a husky, eager young man with a work ethic he had inherited from his Dutch father and German mother. Starting after high school, he worked Gulf oil platforms doing mostly menial work as a roustabout – cleaning the deck, unloading equipment and supplies, painting the sides of the rig from a dangling scaffold, relieving the roughnecks for meal breaks, and doing anything no one else wanted to do. But in the process, he was learning the deep-water oil business from the "ground" up.

Pete shared his work shifts and much of his off time with the crane operator, Mike O'Shaughnessy. Coming up through the ranks of the oil drilling business together, Pete had developed a valued friendship with Mike and his family. And now Pete would be quick to admit—thanks to them he was on his way to recovering from the most tragic event of his life.

Last year Pete's wife Nancy and their three-year-old son Jonah were driving from their home in San Antonio to meet him for a celebration of their fourth wedding anniversary. Shortly after she entered the I-10 freeway, an overworked trucker going the other way had fallen asleep. He lost control of his 18-wheeler and jumped the median. A fuel tanker and seven cars were demolished. Nancy's was one of them.

No one survived the resulting inferno.

Pete was devastated. If it hadn't been for Mike and his family, he would have followed Nancy and Jonah to their graves. Only one thing stayed his hand—Mike and Bridget took him into their home like one of their own.

It took almost a year before the darkness began to fade. Just last month, Pete had been godfather to their first-born, a son. This very human event and the love it signified started him on the road back. He was beginning to feel whole again.

Then, on this gray April afternoon, as if to say, "Oh no, you don't," Hurricane Jane came skipping over the horizon.

By now, Pete had become first mate of the rig and was responsible for all operations on the drilling deck. In his years in the Gulf oil business, he had been through several hurricane alarms without a hit. But with over a hundred platforms in the region, a notorious band of "equipment pirates" had become a real problem for rigs left unguarded.

Mike yelled over the noise of the wind, "Waddya think are the odds that this one'll hit us, Pete? Should we get on that last copter to shore? Them two storms that plowed the Gulf last year didn't come anywhere near us."

"We just got a shipment of new drill pipes and bits," Pete replied. "I ain't about to desert this place while those damn pirates are creepin' round. We'll make sure everything is secured, break out the shotguns, an' ride 'er out! There's still enough of a crew aboard to do the job. But Mike, you've got a wife and my godson to support. So you hurry over an' grab that ride!"

"Nope. If you stay I stay. My old man had thirty years on the rigs—land and sea. Paddy never left one for a storm and I ain't about to neither. 'Sides, if those damn pirates come up here you're gonna need all the help you can get!"

But it wasn't pirates that came aboard. The helicopter with the last of those leaving the rig had gotten less than a half mile away when Jane made her entrance—right in the flight path.

"Here I am, boys. Let's party!"

She sucked the hapless craft into her massive vortex, spun it around a few times and flung it back out—like the last kid on the end of a "crack-the-whip" line. The helicopter full of rig workers broke into a thousand pieces, and each one shot out of the maelstrom at over 100 miles an hour.

Mike paled at the sight of people and debris being flung about like confetti, and at the realization he could have been among them. Watching from the upper deck, he and Pete were too stunned to speak. But they would have had little time to say much because Jane's next move was to engulf the entire rig in her awesome embrace.

Since it was not anchored to the sea floor, Deepwell was like a huge cork. The satellite-controlled thrusters fought valiantly to maintain position but were no match for Jane.

Pete, Mike, and two others of the skeleton crew were

hanging onto the drilling tower struts, intending to repel any pirate who tried to board after the storm passed. But Jane was not just anyone. She tilted the platform, wrapped her arms around people and cargo in a death-hug and swept them all into the angry waves.

Then, in one of her sudden mood changes, she turned docile as the eye of the storm passed over. Choking on seawater, Pete struggled to the surface. He was shaken to see the flat, calm water littered with people and broken debris, while all around him the storm churned like a pride of lions circling its prey.

About fifty feet away, he saw a body floating face down. It had to be Mike—he was the only redhead aboard. Pete tugged a wooden pallet over, and by the time he got the half-drowned man aboard it Mike was sputtering, gagging and vomiting seawater.

"Mike, you crazy oil junkie, you missed getting killed on the chopper so now you're trying to drown yourself!"

Pete knew they had only a few minutes before the other eye wall hit, so he put all his strength into pulling the pallet and its cargo toward the oil rig. They were almost there when Jane decided to lend a hand. This time her winds were swirling in the opposite direction and instead of hurling things out to sea, she slammed them against the rig's hull. Although the wooden pallet Mike was holding onto shattered on impact, it lessened the force of the blow to him. He clung to a large timber until two of the rig workers who had been below deck were able to pull him aboard.

But Pete was not so lucky—he went head first into the hull.

When he was finally able to focus, Pete caught sight of Nancy and Jonah coming toward him over a calm, shining sea.

With a joy and serenity he had never known, Pete got up and met them halfway.

Liza Young

"Words that can never be spoken are given birth in the written word."

Liza Young is a writer of poetry and short stories. She has been published in *The MacGuffin, Oberon Literary Journal, The Pinehurst Journal, Cellar Roots Special Issue—Metropolyesterday Dreams,* and the anthologies *The Space Between, Facets* and *A Velvet Bridge,* and won several writing competitions. She has done readings at the Scarab Club in Detroit and the Detroit Opera House.

Kindred Root

Liza Young

A nameless road's shoulder
and there, among the branches,
a gabled roof—broken, remaining
shingles aching for burial. The doorway, naked
in the sun, two spaces that could have been
windows, leaning hard, doing their best to support
this house, melting into the earth.
The oak tree that sprouted,
a seed beneath the floorboards, slurping
water from a spilt wash tub, or a child's cup,
because there was no milk, absorbing
beams of sunlight pressing through
the windows, floorboards, like gapped
teeth keeping their distance
from each other. They left one day, the family—
a mother, swallowing bitterness given her by a man
too large for the cramped home, six children, always
hungry, dirty from picking beans and peas they weren't
     allowed
to eat. A man who preferred the penitentiary
to this jail. Children, in ill-fitting clothes, education
that of bole weevils and chiggers.
They left, taking all they had—nothing,
leaving the door ajar, windows open, endowing
the worn lumber, the hay mattresses balanced
on rope, the tin cups and rag quilts, to the oak. Giving
it the chance, the house never gave them.

The Depth of Flesh

Liza Young

Lifting her gown that first time,
the leathery parcel of skin sliding
to her side, my disgust enveloped
in a smile. Filling my palm with balm, I slid
my fingers into the crevices, born
at the birth of her twins, the ruts
and gullies of once tight flesh, rippling
like waves. Ridges running the length
of her, cracks like springtime asphalt.
I wanted to do this, to soothe
her, distract the pain with scents
of pears and melon, to find
her hidden navel, but my fingers tangled
in the depth of accordioned flesh.
In a moment, her hand over mine,
and a whisper—don't worry, maybe
you'll take after your dad.

Jill Jack

Jill Jack is an award winning singer/songwriter. She has always loved words. As a child she escaped into the world of reading and writing poetry, short stories and journaling. As she matured, Jill used this passion of writing to become a successful singer/songwriter. Winner of 46 Detroit Music Awards, Jill has released twelve albums of original music, toured with Bob Seger and John Waite. She shared the stage with many national acts such as Emmylou Harris, Dan Fogleberg, Shawn Colvin, just to name a few. Jill has enjoyed a beautiful career filled with wonderful experiences traveling the world.

While Jill has journaled every day since she was 11, she is now re-entering the world of writing short stories, poetry, and also painting. She feels blessed to be able to express herself with so many artistic mediums.

Our Last Coffee

Jill Jack

As the soft hum of the nurses' voices seeped into my father's hospital room, so did the smell of freshly brewed coffee. It was 4 AM, and I had just signed DNR papers per my father's request. As the middle kid from a family of five, the "balance beam" as my mother labeled me, this was my role. Stay calm, objective, somewhat emotionless and do what was requested of me. But here I was, sleep deprived, hand shaking, barely remembering how to hold a pen. Basically, I was signing away any chance of keeping my father alive if he needed resuscitation. The contrasted feelings of denial, fear, and peace were causing my head to spin. He had suffered so much. I did not want to see him in pain anymore. But the thought of him, the patriarch, the oak tree of our family, not being with us anymore was almost too much to bear. Selfishly, I did not want him to die.

I was always nervous being alone with my Dad. We had a disconnect. I think I made him uncomfortable. Or maybe he made me uncomfortable. I had grown into a geographically challenged, slow-learning empath, who detested sarcasm and empty jokes. I only had an artistic brain to offer.

I remember once I invited my parents over to my new home, new to me anyway. The 100-year-old, dilapidated house needed a ton of work. I had recently divorced and purchased all I could afford. I wanted to create a serene space, a place of calm. I refused to install window treatments because I loved natural light. I decided to have no electronics on the main floor. I did own one TV, my grandmother's old box television that I kept in my bedroom upstairs. I filled my home with garbage picked furniture that I lovingly refurbished. Ironically, I found most of this furniture in the garbage of the privileged city I grew up in and where my parents still lived.

I paced back and forth waiting for them to arrive. Their Cadillac edged next to the curb in front of my house. Why were my hands sweating? These are my parents. Looking back, I realize, I wanted to impress them. They came in and immediately plopped down on my newly purchased pottery barn couch. Yes, it was the used floor model, but it was still in good shape. Readjusting my nicely arranged pillows with irritation, they settled, sitting uncomfortably close to each other.

My Dad always reached for something to read or the TV clicker. He looked around and asked, "Where is your TV?"

I explained that I did not like technology and wanted my space peaceful. I stiffened, knowing this ventured into the emotional territory my father loathed. My mother looked down at her hands, obviously anticipating my father's response.

The sarcastic smirk brushed over his face as he responded, "Oh, I see, you want us *to talk*, talk about *our feelings*." So, yes, I guess my dad was as uncomfortable with me as I was him.

The rhythm of the hospital machines that intertwined with my father's slow breathing brought me back to the present. The coffee aroma warmly engulfed the hospital room. With a quiet calm my father said, "That coffee smells so good." I asked if he would like me to get him a cup. He whispered earnestly, "Yes, that would be great."

The nurse brought us two cups of steaming black coffee. I held the cup, breathing in the rich roasted smell, a sadness washed over me. I realized this might be our last cup of coffee together.

Coffee. That, we had in common. I lived at home until I was 27, which gave us plenty of time to bond over coffee. My father and I thrived in the morning, when the rest of the house remained in bed. We often stood shoulder to shoulder watching each drip of beautiful, dark-roasted gold fill the pot. I always wanted to cheat and grab some before it was done brewing, but my father would insist on waiting until the final drip. A respectful silence developed between us, a church-like silence. He poured my cup first, and then his. We slurped in unison, nodded, and went our separate ways to prepare for our day.

When I moved out, he sometimes asked me to come and grab some paperwork for his accountant where I worked. He always started the conversation with, "Come early, and I will put on a big pot of coffee."

That was our thing. So, as we sat sipping our last coffee together, our last moment alone before all the drama of my siblings showing up, my heart broke.

I found it too painful to look at my father. I chose, instead, to admire the floating, dark roast gold in my Styrofoam cup. "Dad, are you sure you really want the DNR?"

Calmly and quietly, he sipped his coffee. And in a voice filled with determined peace, he said, "I have been lying in bed these last five years staring at the ceiling. I have been in excruciating pain. This is not how I imagined living the last years of my life." He then paused, as if rethinking the question. He said "Yes, I am sure."

As the morning sun began to rise amid the shuffling of the early morning shift change, my father closed his eyes, inhaling the last of the aroma of what would be his final cup. I turned my head so he could not see the tears streaming down my face.

Ode to Darla

Jill Jack

I found you sitting on a ledge in a dirty, dingy little motel on the way to my next gig. I did not take a shower, but I took you with me.

The life of a musician on a solo tour can be very lonely. Now, I had a companion.

My heart felt lighter with you staring at me as I drove down the two-lane highway. With reckless abandonment, I turned up the jams, singing "Sweet Caroline" at the top of my lungs. I encouraged you to sing along, but your lips stayed sealed with a big, beautiful smile gracing your face.

We decided to stop for lunch at a wooded rest area. I carefully carried you and my lunch bag, finding the picnic table with the best picturesque view of nature's heaven.

As I dipped my peapods in my hummus, I asked if you loved nature and the beautiful way the sun shone through the trees. I shared with you that I felt nature was the closest thing to God for me. You peacefully smiled back at me. I knew you felt the same way. As I packed up our lunch and carried you back to the van, I realized that I never wanted the road trip to end. I just wanted you and me to keep exploring.

Town to town, gig to gig, we adventured together. You seemed to understand my struggles unwinding after a performance. My adrenaline still flying high, I would walk us back into the next dingy motel and talk about the show. You let me go on and on about how it felt to receive the love and acceptance from the audience. How my songs seem to ring true with these newfound friends. With you resting on my shoulder, providing me a warming comfort, I felt myself give in to the lateness of the night and drift off to sleep.

It was a long drive to the last show of the tour. Pulling into the motel parking lot, I could barely keep my eyes open. I grabbed my guitar, locked the doors, and headed into the grungy motel. I laid my head on the pillow and drifted off to sleep. In my dream, I heard you calling my name. I woke, startled, realizing I left you in the car.

I ran out to the parking lot, and with tears in my eyes, I apologized profusely as I carried you back into the motel room. You laid on the pillow next to me and your forgiving smile calmed me to sleep.

As I rose to take shower the next morning, a sadness washed over me.

It was time to go home.

As I packed the car, I shared what life at home would be like. I really wanted you to feel welcome and comfortable. You would have a beautiful ledge to sit on. My husband Roger was a clean freak so you would not have to worry about dirty bathtubs anymore.

One year later, as the morning sun rose, I dragged my butt out of bed. Wiping the sleep from my eyes, I poured myself a cup of coffee.

I unloaded the clean dishes and loaded the dirty laundry. As I went to jump in the shower, I caught you staring at me from the ledge of the bathtub.

Though your yellow was fading, your smile was still bright as could be peeking out under your orange beak. Mischief twinkled in your eyes as if you were saying, "Come on, let's hit the road sister. It's time."

Nicole e. Castle

Nicole e. Castle teaches composition and literature at Macomb Community College; edits the college's literary magazine, *ARTIFEX*; and hosts a literary reading series called WORDcraft Wednesdays. She is a current member of the board for the Great Lakes Association of Horror (GLAHW) and editor of their horror short fiction and poetry magazine, *Ghostlight: The Magazine of Terror*. She loves Halloween, creepy things (her husband included), and writing. Find out more about GLAHW at: glahw.com.

Last Time in New Orleans

Nicole e. Castle

If I could have dreamt you,
I would have made you
a shimmer of silvery rain
that drenched my hair, chilled my skin,
filled my mouth.
Instead,
I dreamt of dirty streets, at last call and
you as the street sweeper.

Transcendant

Nicole e. Castle

In this place
of flickering lights
I want to kiss you
not out of desire
but to mix my breath with yours
as God did to Adam
as Adam did
to
her.

Above

Nicole e. Castle

On paper, I am god.
And you?
You are a word.
A tiny word, or one hard to spell.

Here, I am ruler.
And you are servant. You are cattle.
You are a thing.
You are whatever I wish
to make you.

Your desires, your flaws, your ugliness,
I make you.
You are born only if I say you are.
You will live, endure, and die when I say.
Or when I do not.

I can erase you.
Mark you out.
Deny you birth—or death.
I can make you a coward, a pestilence, a madman.
I can cry at what I write about you,
or I can laugh at you.

And you will never know,
because you are always flat—black ink on white paper.
And I am always standing above you.

Terry Hojnacki

Terry Hojnacki, author of *I Can See With My Eyes Shut Tight*, is an award-winning flash fiction writer, children's book author, poet, novelist, editor, and lover of words. She is the founder and editor-in-chief of *Sterling Script: A Local Author Collection* which is one of the many ways she works to promote her writing community.

Terry is a member of Detroit Working Writers, Society of Children's Book Writers and Illustrators, Rochester Writers, Sterling Heights Library Board of Trustees, and founder of Tuesday Morning Writers. She is the Creative Writers Workshop facilitator at the Sterling Heights Public Library, where she was named 2018 Volunteer of the Year.

Her short stories and poetry have appeared in *ARTIFEX, Ghostlight: The Magazine of Terror, Pink Panther Magazine, Nicole's Recurring Nightmares,* and *Sterling Script: A Local Author Collection.*

www.TerryHojnacki.com.

The City Below

Terry Hojnacki

The hum of their generators vibrated in my ears every night as I settled in bed. Some nights, metal blades scraped against the clay ground. I imagined workers expanding a city under our city, excavating tunnels to new suburban hubs. I pictured small creatures like ants or voles, but the sounds were so similar to our construction sites I started to see people. People like us. People like us, but with big, dark eyes and pale, dusty skin.

I heard the heavy thump of bass drums at two o'clock in the morning. The percussion dominated, but if I focused, the melancholy melody of the song touched me. Were the people in the under-city there by choice? Did they know about us? *Why was there a city under our city?* I pulled my blanket tight to my shoulders. Snuggled safe, the sad song put me to sleep, night after night.

I had to know if anyone else recognized the sounds from underground, but who could I ask? Mom would say I had a creative imagination. Dad would smile and nod while he tapped the keys on his laptop. Maybe my brother would listen?

"Really, David," I said. "When the traffic noise is almost nonexistent. When everyone's sleeping. Have you ever laid there in your bed and noticed it?"

"Nope, can't say that I have." He chuckled. "But if you

do, Lizzy, it must be pretty cool."

"I'm serious. Motors humming. Music playing. Some nights I've gotten up and opened my window to see if it was louder outside."

"And was it?"

"No, it was weird. It got quieter. But as soon as I tried to go to sleep, it was there. The vibration. The sounds. Like white noise from under the city."

David shrugged. "We have the salt mines in the area. You should try to find out more about them. What if a section near our house is still active?"

I wanted to press him to talk more, but David had offered his explanation.

I thought he might be right, so I did some research on the library computer. There was no record of a mine under our neighborhood. A search for underground cities or lost cities near our house came up blank. I told myself to stop playing the "What If" game.

That night, I went upstairs to my room. Lying in bed, I listened for the familiar hum of the generators I imagined. The train, a few miles away, blew its whistle three times exactly at 12:42 AM, just like it did every Sunday. My ears adjusted back to the quiet as I settled into a twilight sleep. Two more blasts of the train's whistle startled me. The rumbling rhythm of the engines below changed its pattern.

Then it stopped. And my pulse quickened.

In the darkness, red emergency lights flashed through my window and down the hall. I bounded out of bed to see what was happening outside. A swarm of red trucks and black SUVs surrounded our house.

I inhaled to scream when Dad came up behind me and clamped his rough hand over my mouth. He hugged me tight, leaned his lips to my ear, and whispered, "Shh. It's going to be okay."

Through my sheer bedroom curtains, I looked down and

saw an army of camo-clad gunmen get out of the vehicles. They lined up in an arc on our front lawn and started firing. The living room windows blew out; I heard shattered glass crash into the room. Dad spun me away from the terror and pulled me toward the linen closet in the hall.

Mom and David were there, scared and confused.

With the tip of his shoe, Dad touched the molding next to the closet door. The wall slid back, revealing a metal ladder that descended in the center of the old furnace chimney liner. He hugged Mom, handed her a flashlight, and guided her to the first step.

"Go down as fast as you can. We'll be right behind you."

"Where do I meet you?" she asked, stepping onto the top rung.

"At the end of the tunnel." He kissed her cheek. "Go. Quickly!"

David and I followed Mom. Dad closed the access panel and came right after me. When we got to the bottom, the tunnel led away from the house.

Mom stopped and waited for all of us to touch the ground. She reached out for us and sighed.

Dad pushed our huddled group further into the tunnel. "Don't stop. Go. Go. Go." He ordered with increasing urgency. "We're not safe yet!"

Shining the light ahead of her, Mom led the way.

The only sounds in this space were our quick, shuffling feet and heavy breathing. I don't know how far we went before Dad whispered, "Tell Mom she can slow down a bit."

Like the game telephone, I repeated Dad's words to David, and he told Mom.

Instead of slowing "a bit," Mom stopped. She held the flashlight toward the ceiling of the tunnel so it glowed like a soft lamp. She gave Dad a look and said, "What the hell is going on?"

"I didn't say stop. We have to keep moving till we're out

of here."

"We don't even know where here is. John, what the hell is going on?"

"We don't have time, Anna," Dad answered, hushed but firm.

Mom tried to argue when a low, earth-moving groan interrupted her. The splintering noise began far away and grew louder as it seemed to get closer. Like a crack in an ice pond, this one rippled out from the center. And our house was the bull's eye.

"The house is collapsing!" Dad pushed past us, grabbed Mom's hand, and bolted from the sounds of crumbling earth. "Run!"

David and I followed. As we ran, I replayed what Dad had just said. Did our house really implode? I pictured the bookshelves in a heap under the bathtub and my shattered vanity mirror. Splintered wood, a mangled bed frame, under shingles and siding.

The tunnel opened into a large cavern with hanging lights draped across the pathway. The smell of roasted potatoes and warm bread hung in the air. Behind us, I saw the dust cloud from the explosion rolling in as a heavy door slid shut.

A round-faced, stocky woman with a babushka covering her gray hair grabbed my Dad's elbow. "Hurry, John. You've got to hide."

Dad held Mom's hand, and she took mine. David pressed against my back. Squished between my parents and brother, I was carried to a dank hole in the wall. We crammed in and the opening sealed itself.

We all had questions, but Dad shushed us. "Stay quiet."

We stood, our bodies smashed together, with barely enough room for me to squeeze my arm up to scratch my cheek. It smelled like mud, the way you would expect a troll's lair to smell.

Darkness and body heat surrounded me. My bare feet

were cold on the damp ground. I squirmed, repositioning my legs as the pins and needles coursed up the right side. My stomach growled like a roaring lion in the silence. David snickered, and Dad shushed us again.

How long were we going to be sardines hidden in the wall?

I rested my head on Mom's shoulder and closed my eyes. Her arm circled my waist and held me tight. For a second, the reassurance felt good, but the deafening silence unsettled me. My heartbeat sounded like the drum in a marching band booming above my family breathing the musty air. Air. Do we have enough air?

My blood pulsed through my temples, and the pressure on my chest crushed my lungs. I couldn't breathe. I couldn't think. I couldn't die locked in a wall in the city below.

Dad's strong hand squeezed my shoulder, and Mom tightened her hug. I breathed. Slowly. In and out. I smelled a hint of the strawberry shampoo that clung to my hair and focused on the sweet scent.

The earth moved, dirt rained on us, and the entrance slid open, bringing a burst of new air. When we stepped out of our hiding place, the wall closed, leaving no evidence of where we'd been.

"Sorry, I had to make sure you weren't followed." The babushka'ed lady smiled. "Come with me. Now." She guided us through the domed cavern, past makeshift tables and carts filled with root vegetables, sacks of dried beans and grains. We made our way to a hobbit-like entrance carved in the wall between the apothecary and the bakery, and crowded into a tiny kitchen that smelled of drying herbs and lemon balm tea.

Dad wrapped his arm around the woman's shoulders and smashed her face into his chest. "I've missed you so much," he said, squeezing her too tight.

She laughed, squirmed out of his grasp, and said, "Hi, I'm Johnny's sister, Alice."

Wrapping his arms around us, Dad beamed. "And you're finally getting to meet my wife and kids."

Mom pulled away and crossed her arms. Her glare asked, "What have you been keeping from me?"

Alice intercepted. "I wish we could have met a long time ago, but it was too risky." Her eyes glazed as she continued. "Now we have no choice."

Dad shook his head. "I don't know how they made the connection."

"Doesn't matter... We have to evacuate this hub. I'll take you to the Link." She tapped a tile over the counter and the wall turned into a video screen. Alice spoke, "Activate. Evacuation. Code 4A2X," and the screen disappeared into the wall.

My suspicions were true. My aunt lived in the city below. As reality sank in, another realization hit me. Did my internet search bring this on our family?

Mom sat at the table, rubbing her temples.

Dad leaned on the wall next to her. "How can we help, Al?"

"You can't. Everyone knows what to do in the event of discovery. The plan is already in action." Alice opened a lower cabinet and handed me a one-size-fits-all khaki jumpsuit and a pair of sneakers. Grinning, she said, "Beats bare feet and a nightgown."

I wiggled into the jumpsuit, pulled it over my gown, and zipped it up. The shoes fit better than I expected.

She tossed Dad a small, leather satchel. "Give these to your kids."

He nodded and slipped the bag into his shirt pocket. "What about you? How can we help you?"

"I'll be fine." Let's get you out of here. Once you go through the Link, your family will be safe. I'll meet you there as soon as I can."

They hugged. This time it was a warm, loving hug. When

they separated, Alice took Mom's hand and pulled her close. I heard her whisper, "You're in serious danger. Take care of each other. You may need this."

Mom gasped, staring at the palm-sized pistol. "I can't," she stuttered.

"Honey, give it to Lizzy. She can shoot." Dad winked at me. He'd been taking me to the range since I could see over the gun counter. He took the pistol from Mom and put it in my hand. He wrapped my fingers around the grip, and whispered, "Be careful." Then he gave David his Ruger with a couple extra mags. Adjusting the Glock at his waist, he said, "We have to go."

Everyone in the city below moved through the marketplace with quiet intent. Shop keepers signaled orders to their helpers. Everything got packed or tucked within the walls. The spokes of the hub were being closed, one by one.

Alice explained that, if possible, some people would return to this location. "For now, we take what we can carry and bug out."

She led us down a short corridor to a rectangular alcove no bigger than my bedroom. Or what used to be my bedroom. We walked into the space and faced two elevators with doors that opened from the center.

"Here we are," Alice said. "Our access to the Link. This is where I send you off, Johnny." Tapping his shirt pocket, she said, "Don't forget your kids need their rings to travel the Link."

"You're staying here?"

"You know how it is, the captain is the last one to leave the ship." She took Dad's hand and pulled him close. "Take the next available Link. The destination coordinates are already programmed and will take you to the mountains. There's an established surface community where you'll blend in." Alice winked. "See you soon," she said and hurried back to the marketplace.

A young couple with two small children, carrying backpacks and bags, rushed toward the alcove. "Excuse us," the woman said, brushing past Mom. A little girl held the strap of the woman's bag tight and stayed close.

Dad ushered us out of their way.

The man, holding a toddler in his arm, passed his hand over the access panel between the two elevators. Less than a minute later, the one on the left opened. When his family was aboard, he repeated the motion, and the doors closed.

Dad took the bag from his pocket and pulled out two rings. "These rings give you the ability to travel on any Link across the planet." He handed one to David, and the other to me. "Don't lose your ring, or you'll be stuck at your last location. Only you can use your ring."

"But there's only two," David said. "What about you and Mom?"

Dad put his arm around Mom. "Our wedding bands are already coded." He held her close and kissed her cheek.

We put our rings on as Dad passed his hand over the panel.

Our Link opened at the same time as the one the family had just used. A squad of uniformed gunmen charged out, weapons ready. Dad shoved me in our Link. Mom pushed David into me as the bullets flew. Dad reached out and swung his ring by the access panel. I screamed a helpless scream.

David and I watched our parents gunned down in front of us.

I collapsed. My whole body vibrated. It felt like every one of my cells was a tiny piece of jello, uncontrollably jiggling. We were safe. On our way to wherever Alice programmed the Link to take us. David slouched, cross-legged next me, his arm draped over my shoulders.

My mind replayed the scene. Over and over. I saw the bullets hitting Mom. In the arm. In the stomach. In her chest.

I saw Dad reaching for her as he activated our Link. The shot that jolted his body. The look on his face as he fell to the ground. And I know he saw my horror as the Link doors closed.

When the program was complete and the entrance opened, moonlight flickered through tall pines and danced in my lap. Cool, mountain air filled my lungs as the music of cicadas and katydids greeted us. We stepped out of the Link and looked up at the enormous star-filled sky.

Tapestry

Terry Hojnacki

Spread across the cutting table, flaws in the fabric of my life glare like demons taunting me. I snatch silver scissors from the tray and clip withered webs of unwanted folds. snip by snip, removing snags, splotched dyes, and tiny tears until all that's left is a holey mess of scraps. even the good parts have lost their beauty. reduced to a pile of sad rags tossed in a basket, the shredded cloth challenges me. I thread the needle. one seam, then another, stitch small swatches of material together like puzzle pieces to make it whole again. finally frayed, worn, wrinkled remnants of unique character, sewn with gold fiber, restore beauty to the tapestry of my life.

Previous editions of
Sterling Script: A Local Author Collection

released in 2018, 2019, & 2020
are available on Amazon.com
and through localauthorcollection@gmail.com.

ABOUT

Sterling Script: A Local Author Collection

Like us on Facebook at
https://www.facebook.com/LocalAuthorCollection

Would you like your flash fiction, short stories, poetry, art,
or creative nonfiction considered for publication
in our next volume?
Email **localauthorcollection@gmail.com**
to be placed on our mailing list.

Submission dates and guidelines for the
2022 edition of Sterling Script
COMING SOON

.

Made in the USA
Monee, IL
11 November 2021

81639910R00104